Practice Companion

VOLUME 2

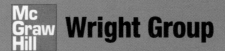
McGraw Hill Wright Group

The McGraw·Hill Companies

www.WrightGroup.com

Send all inquiries to:
Wright Group/McGraw-Hill
P.O. Box 812960
Chicago, IL 60681

ISBN 978-0-07-656533-7
MHID 0-07-656533-5

1 2 3 4 5 6 7 8 9 RMN 14 13 12 11 10

Contents

Unit 6

Unit 7

Unit 8

Week ④

Focus Question

How do brains and
muscles work together to
help people succeed?

My Weekly Planner

Week of _____

Theme Vocabulary	_____
Differentiated Vocabulary	_____
Comprehension Strategy and Skill	Strategy: _____ Skill: _____
Vocabulary Strategy	_____
Spelling Skill	_____
Fluency	Selection: _____
Writing and Language Arts	Writing form: _____
Grammar	Grammar skill: _____

Related Words

You can use related words to help you define a word.

Word: **life**   Related word: **activities**

Sentence: My life is full of after-school activities.

Word: **settle**   Related word: **house**

Sentence: Our family will settle in a house in the town.

Word: **suburb**   Related word: **city**

Sentence: We live in a suburb of a big city.

Write a related word on the line. Then write a sentence. The first item has been done for you.

1. Word: **life**   Related word: day

   Sentence: Every day of my life, I eat.

2. Word: **settle**   Related word:

   Sentence: _____

   _____

3. Word: **suburb**   Related word:

   Sentence: _____

   _____

Word Associations and Related Words

life	settle	suburb

Write the related word. The first item has been done for you.

1. Which vocabulary word is related to
   breathing? life_____

2. Which vocabulary word is related to a *place outside a big city?* _____

3. Which vocabulary word is related to *moving in?* _____

4. Which vocabulary word is related to *alive?*
   _____

5. Which vocabulary word is related to *staying?*
   _____

6. Which vocabulary word is related to *lots of space?* _____

Words with *str*, *spr*, *scr*, and *spl*

stripe	scream	spring	splash	school
string	scrap	spray	split	through

Write letters to complete the words.

1. A skunk has a white __str__ipe down his back.

2. A skunk might _____ay a dog that gets close.

3. We heard a _____eam that hurt our ears.

4. My friend forgot her lunch, so I _____it mine with her.

5. We need _____ing to fly our kite.

6. We wrote a note on a _____ap of paper.

7. Look _____ough your homework before you hand it in.

8. My dog made a big _____ash in the pool.

9. We saw a rabbit _____ing out from behind the fence.

10. At _____ool today we learned three new words.

4

Poem

Read this poem aloud.

One Hundred Years Ago
by Robin Ghent

Let's stop to think about life long ago.
How were things different?
What do you know?

What would you do without a TV?
There'd be no computer or movies to see.

Without a cell phone, would you feel all alone?
Or would you go visit a friend at his home?

You wouldn't be riding on busses or trains.
Nor could you travel by car or by plane.

And what would you do when day became night?
Perhaps you would find a candle to light.

One thing we'll learn and then we will know,
How different life was a long time ago.

How well did you read? Circle your answer.

Summarize

When you **summarize**, you tell the most important ideas in a selection in your own words.

Read the story. Look for important ideas.

In the 1800s, farm families drove into town in their horse-drawn wagons to shop. Mothers bought flour, salt, and other goods at the general store. Children might buy a few pieces of hard candy. At the hardware store, fathers bought nails, tools, and other supplies. At the end of the day, families would load everything into their wagons and head for home.

Write the most important ideas. Use the ideas to write a summary.

Idea	**Idea**	**Idea**
In the 1800s, farm families drove their wagons into town to shop.	They bought food and other goods at the general store.	They bought such things as nails and tools in the hardware store.

Summary

Long ago, families drove their wagons into town. They bought goods and supplies at the general store and the hardware store.

Read this story and look for important ideas.

In the 1800s, many children worked hard. In the cities, they sold newspapers or delivered groceries. They even worked in factories. In the country, they planted crops and took care of farm animals. They did many other chores around the farm. When their work was done, they found time to play and do their homework.

Write three important ideas. Then write a summary in your own words.

Idea	Idea	Idea

Summary

Analogies

Analogies compare the way one pair of things is related to another pair of things. An analogy can help you picture something in your mind.

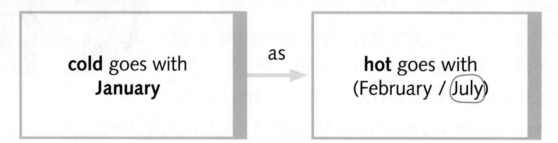

What two pairs of things are being compared? The analogy helps you picture the weather (cold and hot) and the months (January and July) when that weather happens.

Read this analogy.

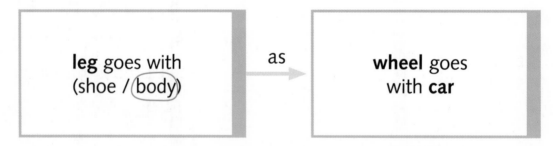

What two pairs of things are being compared? The analogy helps you picture the parts of things (leg and wheel) and the things (body and car) that they are parts of.

Circle the word that completes the analogy.

box goes with **square** — as → **ball** goes with (round / bounce)

puppy goes with (lion / dog) — as → **kitten** goes with **cat**

bread goes with (butter / ice cream) — as → **cereal** goes with **milk**

baseball goes with **bat** — as → **tennis ball** goes with (football / racket)

Categorize and Classify

When you **categorize and classify**, you put things that are alike into a group.

Fruits	**Vegetables**
apples, grapes, bananas	carrots, peas, corn

- The name of a category tells what is in that group.
- The things in a category are examples.

Each group of words tells something about a category. Write the name for each category.

Buildings   Family Members   Sports   Subjects

Buildings
fire station
library
police station

_____
baseball
soccer
kickball

_____
math
science
reading

_____
mother
father
sister
brother

10

Unit 5, Project 1

Inquiry Planner

My Plan for Next Week

1. The Inquiry question is:

_____

_____

2. What information will I collect?

_____

3. How will I collect information?

☐ Books   ☐ Talking to people

☐ Other _____

4. Where will I collect information?

☐ My classroom   ☐ My school library
☐ At home   ☐ In my community

☐ Other _____

5. When will I collect information?

☐ During Self-Selected Reading time
☐ During Independent Practice time
☐ After school

Picture Book

What is a picture book?

- A picture book tells a story or explains a topic or idea.

- A picture book has drawings or photographs.

- A picture book uses words to help tell the story.

- A picture book has a cover with a title and the name of an author.

My Notes: _____

_____

_____

_____

_____

_____

Focus Question
What was life like in the past?

What was life like in the past for the people you read about?
Fill in the wheel with examples of how they lived.

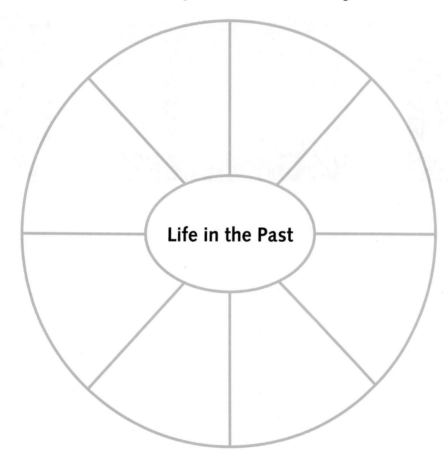

Life in the Past

How do communities change, and how do they
stay the same? Write your answer.

_____

_____

_____

Focus Question

What are communities like today?

What can you see in a community today that you wouldn't have seen in the past? Write your answer.

_____

_____

_____

_____

My Weekly Planner

Week of _____

Theme Vocabulary	_____
Differentiated Vocabulary	_____
Comprehension Strategy and Skill	Strategy: _____ Skill: _____
Vocabulary Strategy	_____
Spelling Skill	_____
Fluency	Selection: _____
Writing and Language Arts	Writing form: _____
Grammar	Grammar skill: _____

Advertisement

Read this advertisement aloud.

Green Valley
by Dale Wahl

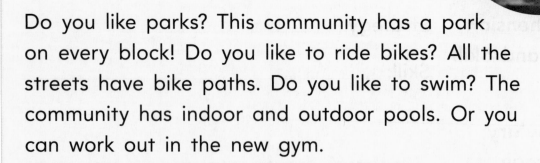

If you are looking for a great place to live, you can stop looking! The Green Valley planned community has it all.

Do you like parks? This community has a park on every block! Do you like to ride bikes? All the streets have bike paths. Do you like to swim? The community has indoor and outdoor pools. Or you can work out in the new gym.

The community has a new school. You can walk to many stores and restaurants. Green Valley even has a movie theater.

Green Valley has everything you want and need. Green Valley has everything planned for you!

How well did you read? Circle your answer.

Word Map

Writing about a word and drawing it can help you understand its meaning.

To fill in the box:

- Write a definition.
- Give examples.
- Draw a picture.
- Write a sentence.

Fill in the boxes for the words _history_ and _future_.

What Each Word Means	Examples of Each Word
_____	_____
_____	_____

Word

history
future

Picture	Sentence
	_____
	_____
	_____

Classify Words

Someone or something ordinary is usual or commonly seen. Someone or something famous is well known for being different or special in some way.

Write the word *ordinary* or the word *famous* in the center of the Word Wheel.

Then fill in the wheel with words about ordinary activities in your life or about someone famous.

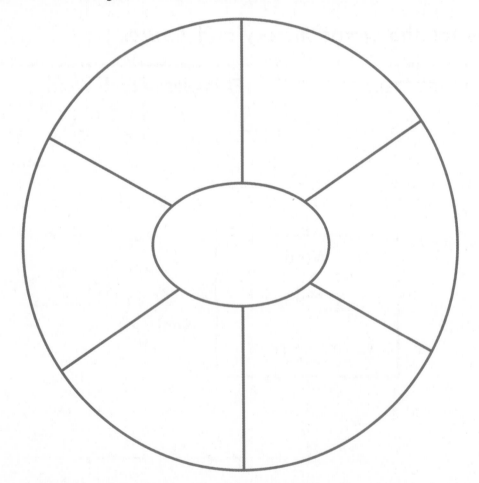

Words with the /ow/ Sound

cow	brown	count	ground	found
howl	down	ouch	mouse	about

Write the spelling words in alphabetical order.
Then draw a line to the correct definition.

1. about _____

2. _____

3. _____

4. _____

5. _____

6. _____

7. _____

8. _____

9. _____

10. _____

a. to say numbers in order

b. an adult female of cattle

c. almost, more or less

d. the color of wood

e. the past tense of *find*

f. the opposite of *up*

g. a small, furry animal

h. the surface of the earth

i. a cry of pain

j. the sound a wolf makes

Monitor Comprehension

As you read, keep checking your understanding. If you don't understand something, use a strategy or several strategies that will help you:

- Reread more slowly.
- Look up words.
- Look for clues in the text.
- Look for clues in the pictures.
- Read on.

**Read the sentences and look at the picture.
Fill in the chart below.**

Lewis Hine was a photographer who lived about a hundred years ago. He felt sad that children worked in factories and mills. He visited many factories across the country. He took pictures of children working. His photographs made people pass laws against child labor.

Part I Didn't Understand	What I Did to Help
1. What does a photographer do?	1. I read on and found out that a photographer takes pictures.
2. What is child labor?	2. I looked *labor* up in a dictionary. It means "work."

Read the sentences and look at the picture.
Then fill in the chart.

Emma was watching the evening news. A story about a bad flood came on. Many families lost all that they owned. The children didn't have clothing or toys. Emma felt sorry for the children. She wondered how she could help.

Part I Didn't Understand	What I Did to Help

The next day, Emma talked to her teacher. They planned a clothing and toy drive for the flood victims. Kids brought in their used clothing and toys. Parents helped ship them to the people in the flood. Emma felt proud that she had been able to help.

Part I Didn't Understand	What I Did to Help

Classify Words

When you **classify** words, you put them in groups or categories. Putting words in groups helps you understand and remember what the words mean.

Look at the groups of words. Add the words to the correct group.

tops	computer	television	cart	horse

Past

oil lamps
log cabins
cart and horse
tops

Today

car
supermarket
cell phone
computer
television

Look at the words below. Add the words to the correct group.

mall	bike	train	car
bus	hospital	hotel	supermarket

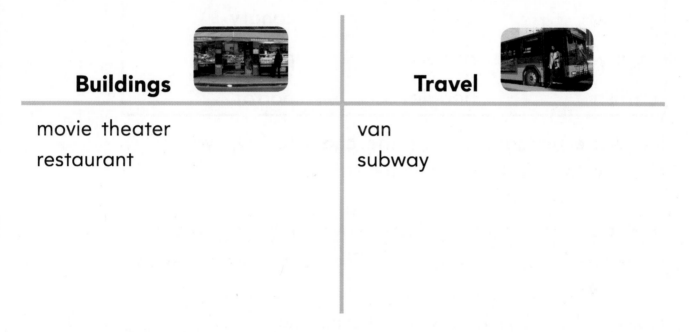

Buildings

movie theater
restaurant

Travel

van
subway

Use the chart to help you answer these questions.

1. How are buildings today different from those in the past?

_____

_____

2. How are the ways to travel today different from those in the past?

_____

_____

Categorize and Classify

When you **categorize and classify**, you put things that are alike into the same group.

Pets		
Fish	**Dogs**	**Birds**
goldfish	collie	canary
guppy	poodle	parakeet
catfish	beagle	parrot

Read the paragraph. Use the chart to help you classify the kinds of transportation.

People can travel in many ways. They can travel on roads by car, bus, or van. They can also travel by rail. Trains can take people through mountains. In cities, subways and elevated trains can move quickly. The fastest way to travel is in the air—in small planes, passenger jets, and jumbo jets.

Transportation		
Roads	**Rails**	**Air**

Focus Question
What are communities like today?

What is life like today in the community you read about? Fill in the "Then and Now" chart comparing the community in the past and the community today.

Then	Now
School	
Transportation	
Jobs/Work	
Housing	

How do communities change and how do they stay the same? Write your answer.

_____

_____

Focus Question
How have people changed their communities?

What kinds of changes can make a community a better place to live? Make a list.

1. _____

_____

2. _____

_____

3. _____

_____

Study the Model

Report

Read the Writing Model along with your teacher. Look for an introduction, middle paragraphs, and a conclusion as well as time order words.

The Telephone
by Jenna Williams

Who invented the telephone? In the early 1870s Alexander Graham Bell had an idea for the telephone. He was experimenting with electricity. He believed he could send the human voice over wires. He got his friend Thomas A. Watson to help. They spent a long time experimenting. In 1876 they discovered how to do it. People were amazed by Bell's invention!

A year later business people had private lines connecting their homes and offices. The Bell Telephone Company was made. Bell predicted that in the future, wires would connect cities and people would talk to each other across the country.

Study the Model

Report

Bell's prediction was correct. In a few years, nearby cities were connected by telephone lines. By 1892 the cities of New York and Chicago were connected. By 1915 telephone lines stretched across the country.

Nearly 100 years after Bell invented the telephone, Martin Cooper invented the cell phone in 1973. Cell phones do not use wires. They send the sound through the air.

The telephone changed people's lives. Today there are different kinds of telephones. They let us talk to people anywhere. We can use them almost anytime. What changes to the telephone will the future bring?

Evaluation Rubric

Report

Writing Trait	Goals	Yes	Needs work!	Now it's OK.
Organization	My report includes an introduction, middle paragraphs, and a conclusion.			
Ideas	I use facts and details that explain my topic.			
Voice	The voice is right for my audience.			
Word Choice	I use pronouns instead of nouns for variety. I use time order words.			
Sentence Fluency	The beginnings of my sentences vary.			
Conventions	All the words are spelled correctly. I use correct punctuation. I use pronouns correctly.			

Peer Review

Report

Read your partner's paper. Then finish each sentence.

1. The topic of this report is

_____

_____ .

2. Some examples of pronouns in the report are

_____

_____ .

3. The writer uses time order words like

_____

_____ .

Name of Reader _____

Subject Pronouns

> A **pronoun** is a word that takes the place of a noun.
>
> A **subject pronoun** replaces a noun in the subject of a sentence. The subject is the part of a sentence that is doing something.
>
> I   you   he   she   it   we   they

Circle the subject in each sentence. Write a pronoun to replace the noun.

1. (The students) read a book about our town.   They

2. My sister will help clean up the park.   _____

3. My friend and I help at the soup kitchen.   _____

Write the word *singular* or *plural* for each pronoun. Write a sentence using the pronoun.

Pronoun	Singular or Plural?	Sentence
I	singular	I ride my bike to school.
she		
they		

Pronouns in Predicates

Some pronouns are used in the **predicate** part of the sentence. These pronouns receive the action of the verb.

Singular	**Plural**
You surprised <u>me</u>.	Mike wants to visit <u>us</u>.
We helped <u>her</u>.	Did you call <u>them</u>?
I like <u>him</u>.	

Write the best pronoun to complete each sentence in the paragraph.

Katy invited (us / we) <u>us</u> to her birthday party. We all brought presents, and Katy opened (them / they) _____ . My present for Katy was a book, and she thanked (I / me) _____ for it. Her dad gave Katy a kitten, and she hugged (he / him) _____ . Her grandparents called (her / she) _____ to say happy birthday.

Taking Tests

Here is a question about *Unlock the Past—Build the Future:*

What is a key to unlocking the past? (Page 7)

Ⓐ planting a community garden

Ⓑ working at a soup kitchen

Ⓒ building a new bridge

Ⓓ looking at old photographs

> **What is the question asking for? An example of a key to unlocking the past.**
>
> A key helps you open a door. So a key to unlocking the past helps you unlock, or open, a door to information. The key helps you learn something.
>
> Read and think about each answer choice.
>
> Look back at page 7 in *Unlock the Past—Build the Future* to confirm your answer. Reread if necessary. Then make a black mark to fill in the circle for the correct answer. Try not to mark outside the circle.

Look at the questions on the next page.

Taking Tests

1. **What important information is in paragraph 1 on page 8?** (Page 8)

   (A) It took a lot of time to get anywhere.
   (B) You couldn't just hop on a subway.
   (C) You probably rode in a cart pulled by a horse.
   (D) Family members stand in front of their cart.

2. **What strategy would you use on page 16 if you didn't know what a streetcar looked like?** (Page 16)

   (A) Look up the meaning of the word *suburb*.
   (B) Look at the old photograph on the page.
   (C) Reread the text.
   (D) Read the caption in the blue box.

3. **When does the time line show that settlers arrived in Portland, Oregon?** (Page 26)

   (A) In 1845
   (B) In the 1850s
   (C) in the 1920s
   (D) in 1939–1945

4. **What can you predict from reading the chapter "Yesterday, Today, and Tomorrow"?** (Pages 24–27)

   (A) Your community will have high-speed trains.
   (B) There will be more museums.
   (C) Your community will have more technology.
   (D) There will be jets everywhere.

My Weekly Planner

Week of _____

Theme Vocabulary	_____
Differentiated Vocabulary	_____
Comprehension Strategy and Skill	Strategy: _____ Skill: _____
Vocabulary Strategy	_____
Spelling Skill	_____
Fluency	Selection: _____
Writing and Language Arts	Writing form: _____
Grammar	Grammar skill: _____

Speech

Read this speech aloud.

Lady Bird
by Del Goldberg

Did you know that people used to throw their trash right on the street? They would also throw trash from their car windows. It would land on the highway. Trash made the streets and highways ugly. It also made them dirty. Bugs and rats would come to eat the trash.

Now, people get a fine if they throw trash out on the street or out of their car window. The fine means they have to pay money. Things didn't change right away. It takes a lot of work to change how people act.

Who helped make this change? Lady Bird Johnson did. She was the wife of President Johnson. With her help, people began planting flowers and removing trash. Soon more people joined in to help. Thanks to Lady Bird, America is much more beautiful.

How well did you read? Circle your answer.

Word Pairs/Related Words

> These are some of the ways words can be related:
>
> - **Synonyms** are words that have almost the same meaning.
>
> - **Antonyms** are words that have opposite meanings.
>
> - **Related words** can be linked in other ways.

Complete each sentence with the word *amazing* or *village*. The first item has been done for you.

1. A synonym for *surprising* is <u>amazing</u>.

2. A related word for _____ is *people.*

3. An antonym for _____ is *boring.*

4. A synonym for _____ is *town.*

5. *Shocking* is a synonym for _____.

Sentences

amazing	village

Write two sentences for each vocabulary word.
One has been done for you.

1. <u>My grandmother told me about the village where she was born.</u>

2. _____

_____

3. _____

4. _____

_____

Write a sentence using both of the vocabulary words.

_____

_____

Words with the /oi/ Sound

foil	point	enjoy	soy	would
join	noise	toy	avoid	could

Read the sentences. Write the word that makes sense in each sentence.

point join **1.** Ms. Lee asked me to join _____ the team.

could would **2.** My friend asked whether I _____ run as fast as he can.

toy noise **3.** I gave my brother a _____ truck for his birthday.

foil soy **4.** My mom wrapped our sandwiches in _____ to keep them warm.

enjoy avoid **5.** We wash our hands to _____ spreading germs.

point toy **6.** I scored a _____ in the game on Saturday.

toy soy **7.** My sister drinks _____ milk.

noise point **8.** The _____ of the thunder woke me up.

Make Predictions

When you **make a prediction**, you tell what you think will happen next. To make a prediction:

- Use information that the author gives.

- Use what you already know.

- Make a best guess about what will happen next.

- Change or adjust your prediction as you read.

Making predictions helps you understand and remember what you read.

Look at the picture and the title of the story. Make a prediction in the chart.

A Pet for Johanna

What I See	What I Predict
The title is *A Pet for Johanna*. The picture shows a young girl holding a cat.	I predict that this book will be about a girl who gets a pet. I think that the pet will be a cat.

Read this story and make predictions.

1. Begin reading. What do you think this story will be about?

Lost and Found Puppy

One morning, Ted went to feed his new puppy, Snuffy. Ted couldn't find Snuffy anywhere.

_____

_____

2. Finish reading the story. Was your prediction correct? If not, change it.

Ted and his mom searched for Snuffy all over the house and the yard. Ted's mom said that Snuffy might have gone to a neighbor's yard. She helped Ted make signs to put up around the neighborhood. The signs said: Help Find Snuffy. Call 555.344.9673.

A day passed. Nobody called about Snuffy. Then, the next morning, the phone rang. Mr. Jackson from down the street said that he just found a white puppy in his garage. It must have been there all night.

"We found Snuffy!" Ted yelled with excitement.

_____

_____

Synonyms and Antonyms

Synonyms are words that have the same, or nearly the same, meaning. **Antonyms** are words that have opposite, or nearly opposite, meanings.

Read the synonyms in the circles. Read the antonyms in the boxes.

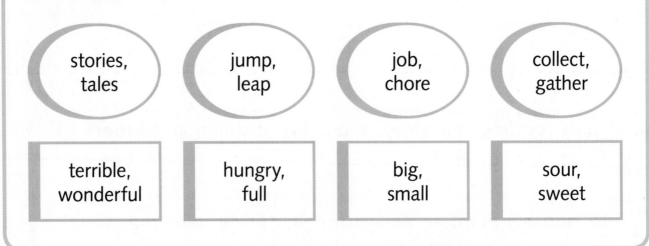

Rewrite the sentences. Replace a circled word with a synonym. Replace a boxed word with an antonym.

1. Joe helped do (jobs) on the farm.

   Joe helped do chores on the farm.

2. Kenny walked along the [empty] streets.

   Kenny walked along the crowded streets.

Rewrite the sentences. Replace a circled word with a synonym. Replace a boxed word with an antonym.

1. My grandfather tells (stories) about when he was young.

_____

_____

2. He grew up on a [big] farm in Ohio.

_____

_____

3. Every morning, he would (collect) eggs from the chicken coop.

_____

_____

4. After school, he helped feed the [full] cows in the barn.

_____

_____

5. Grandfather says it was a [terrible] way to grow up.

_____

_____

Before and After Reading

Read these statements about *Kumak's Fish*.
Write a check mark if you agree. Write an X if
you don't agree.

Before	Kumak's Fish	After
	This story probably takes place in the rain forest.	
	Children learn important skills from their parents.	
	If you don't at first succeed, try, try again.	
	One person can't always do things alone.	
	A community working together can do amazing things.	

Setting

The **setting** of a story tells

- where the story takes place
- when the story takes place

Read the story. Answer the questions about the setting.

Logan opened the door of the log cabin. He peered out into the woods. The sun was low in the sky. Logan's father was out hunting for food.

Logan came back into the cabin. His mother sat near the fire at her spinning wheel. Logan saw that the woodpile was low. He went outside to get logs.

Then he saw his father come into the clearing around the cabin. He carried three rabbits. The family would have a big dinner.

1. Where does the story takes place?

   The story takes place _____

   _____

2. When does the story takes place? What tells you?

   The story takes place _____

   _____

   _____

Kumak's Fish

Think about what you read in *Kumak's Fish*.
Then answer these questions.

1. Do you wish you could have been fishing with
   Kumak that day? Tell why or why not.

   _____

   _____

   _____

2. What stories have you read that are like this one?

   _____

   _____

   _____

3. What was your favorite picture in the book?
   Describe the picture and tell why you liked it.

   _____

   _____

   _____

Draw Conclusions

To **draw conclusions**:

- Use details and facts from the text.

- Use what you already know.

Read the story. Use a story detail and what you know to draw a conclusion.

Many pioneers rode in wagon trains to the West. The wagon trains passed through dangerous places. At night, all the wagons formed a circle. People cooked over open fires in the middle of the circle. Children played inside the circle until bedtime. In the morning, the wagons started out again.

Why did the wagons form a circle at night?

Story Detail: Wagon trains passed through dangerous places.

What I Know: _____

_____

Conclusion: _____

_____

Unit 5, Project 2

Inquiry Planner

My Plan for Next Week

1. The Inquiry question is:

   _____

   _____

2. What information will I collect?

   _____

3. How will I collect information?

   ☐ Books   ☐ Talking to people

   ☐ Other _____

4. Where will I collect information?

   ☐ My classroom   ☐ My school library
   ☐ At home   ☐ In my community

   ☐ Other _____

5. When will I collect information?

   ☐ During Self-Selected Reading time
   ☐ During Independent Practice time
   ☐ After school

Focus Question
How have people changed their communities?

Think about the person whose story you read. How did this person help make a change in the community? Fill in the organizer.

Change <u>name</u> wanted

What _____ did

What _____ did

What _____ did

How can people change their communities?
Write your answer.

_____

_____

49

How do people entertain themselves these days? Fill in the concept web with examples from your community.

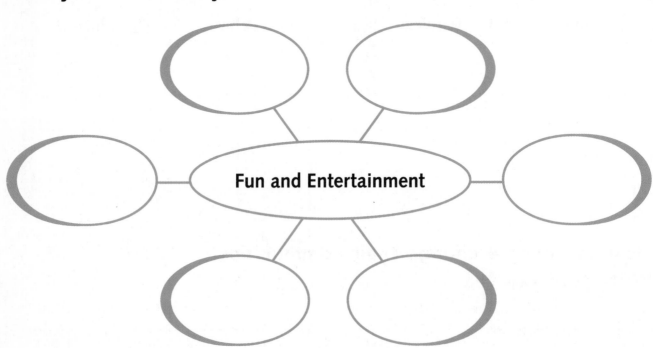

Fun and Entertainment

My Weekly Planner

Week of _____

Theme Vocabulary	_____
Differentiated Vocabulary	_____
Comprehension Strategy and Skill	Strategy: _____ Skill: _____
Vocabulary Strategy	_____
Spelling Skill	_____
Fluency	Selection: _____ _____
Writing and Language Arts	Writing form: _____ _____
Grammar	Grammar skill: _____ _____

Newspaper Article

Read this newspaper article aloud.

Books of the Future?
by Suzy Gerrard

Books have been around for a long time. For many years, the look of a book has not changed very much at all. The books today look a lot like the books your great, great grandparents had.

Now, e-books are becoming popular. E-readers can hold as many books as you can fit on a bookcase. You can even read e-books on cell phones. You can buy e-books on the Internet for very little money. Some are free.

Without paper books, schools, libraries, and bookstores might be very different. So, will e-books change your community? Young people will decide!

How well did you read? Circle your answer.

Scenario

Finish the story by filling in the vocabulary words.

life	settle	suburb	history
future	amazing	village	

One evening, Sunita's father told the family a story about his parents. They left their _____ in India. They came to the United States to start a new _____. They decided to _____ in New York City.

The city was an _____ place to them. They had never been on subways or seen skyscrapers before. After several years, they moved to a _____ in New Jersey. A year later, my father was born.

Sunita's father showed the family photographs of his parents. Sunita looked a lot like her grandmother! Then Sunita's father got his camera. He took pictures of everyone. He said that in the _____ he would show the pictures to his grandchildren.

That is how Sunita learned some of her family's _____.

Connect Words

Answer each question. Use the vocabulary words in your answer.

1. What **amazing** thing do you think may happen in the **future**?

In the future, I think we will have amazing robots that do our work.

2. How is a **suburb** similar to a **village**?

_____

_____

3. When did people begin to **settle** in your community?

_____

_____

4. What **amazing** fact have you learned about **history**?

_____

_____

/air/ Spelled *are*, *air*, *ear*

care	square	fair	wear	scared
share	hair	chair	bear	where

Sort the spelling words. Write them on the lines.

are	air	ear	ere
care			

Finish each sentence with two spelling words.

1. When I saw the big, brown _____,
   I was _____.

2. I don't think it's _____ that I have
   to _____ my room.

3. Please tell me _____ I can find a
   _____ to sit on.

Determine Important Information

Important information tells something about the big ideas in a text. When you read:

- Look for clues such as examples.

- Ask yourself whether the examples are clues to an important idea.

Read this story. Find the big idea.

The city of Hoboken, New Jersey, has changed in many ways. Young people have moved in and fixed up old apartments. New restaurants and shops have sprung up on the main street. A new rail line makes it easy to get from one part of the city to another. Hoboken was always a nice place to live. Now it's a great place to live.

Important Big Idea

Hoboken has changed in many ways.

Read this story. Fill in the web.

Would you like to make your community a better place? Kids can help their communities in many ways. Kids can work in community gardens to grow healthful food. Kids can help with environmental projects such as planting trees and picking up litter. Kids can help other people by visiting senior citizens or reading to younger children. In a community, everyone's actions count.

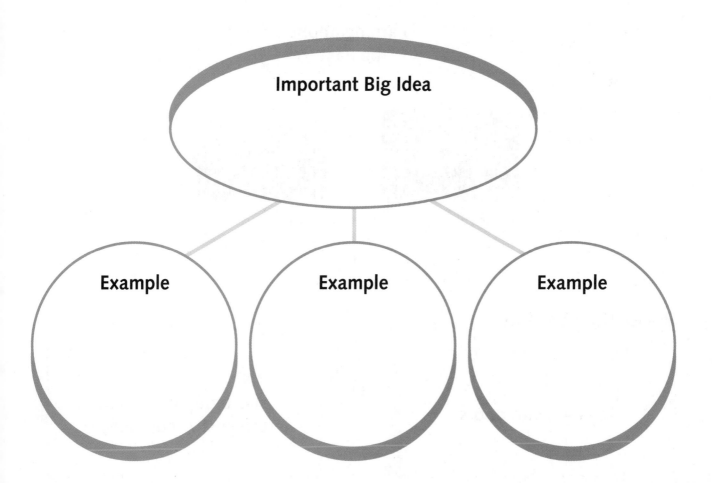

Important Big Idea

Example

Example

Example

Use Multiple Strategies

To **classify** means to put words into groups or categories. The categories can be things, actions, or ideas.

A concept wheel is one way to classify words.

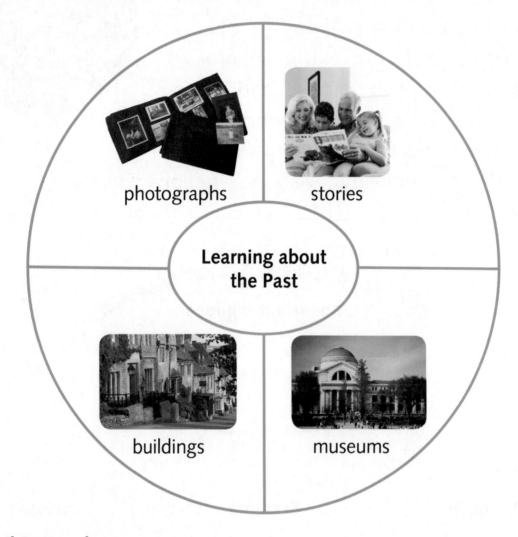

Learning about the Past

photographs

stories

buildings

museums

Read this analogy.

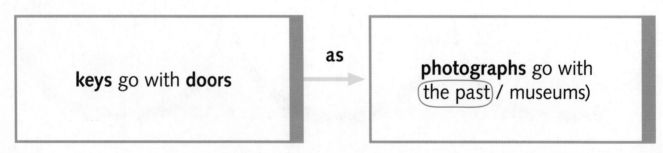

keys go with doors **as** **photographs** go with (the past / museums)

58

Look at the concept wheel about community volunteers. Add another example of something that community volunteers do.

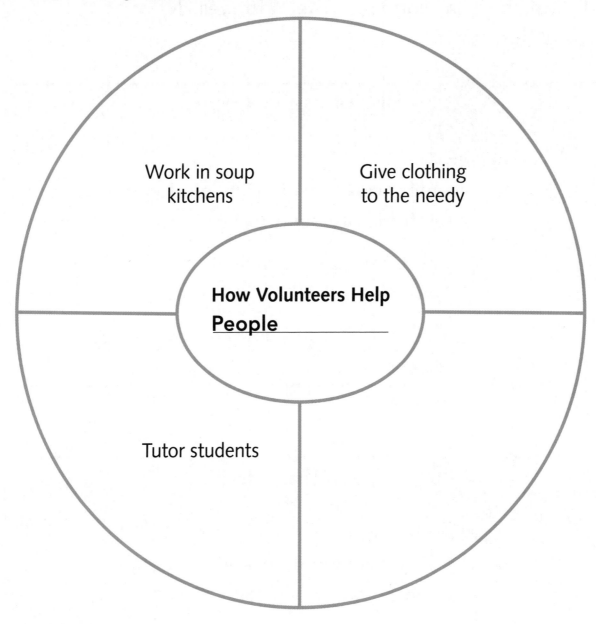

Work in soup kitchens

Give clothing to the needy

How Volunteers Help People

Tutor students

Read this analogy.

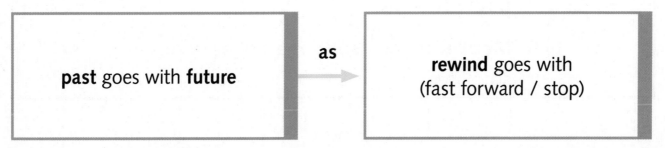

past goes with future

as

rewind goes with (fast forward / stop)

Before and After Reading

Read the sentences and decide whether you think that they are correct. Write **Y** for yes, **N** for no, or **M** for maybe.

Before	Up, Up, and Away	After
_____	**1.** Inventors got the idea for airplane wings from **watching birds**.	_____
_____	**2.** A jumbo jet can carry more than 400 people.	_____
_____	**3.** Helicopters can stay in one spot while in the air.	_____

Before	Over the Wires	After
_____	**1.** The first telephone calls were made through human operators.	_____
_____	**2.** Land-line telephones send messages through wires.	_____
_____	**3.** Mobile phones send messages through satellites.	_____

Spreading the News

Before		After
_____	**1.** Long ago, newspapers were written by hand.	_____
_____	**2.** People used to sit around a radio the way they sit around a television set today.	_____
_____	**3.** People watched Neil Armstrong walk on the moon on live television.	_____

That's Entertainment

Before		After
_____	**1.** People have been playing checkers for 3,000 years.	_____
_____	**2.** By 1860, most homes in America had television sets.	_____
_____	**3.** The Internet has made the world a village because it brings people together from all over the world.	_____

Draw Conclusions

A writer doesn't tell us everything. A reader has to **draw conclusions** about the missing information.

To draw a conclusion:

- Ask yourself a question about the text.

- Use details and facts from the text.

- Use what you already know.

Read the story. Draw a conclusion.

My mom bought a computer. She said that it would be for my sister and me. She wanted to try it out first. Mom carried the computer to the kitchen table. An hour later, my sister asked to try it. She carried it to the porch and e-mailed her friends. Later, I carried it to the family room to play a game.

What kind of computer did the family get?

Detail: The mother used the computer on the kitchen table.

Detail: _____

What I Know: _____

Conclusion: _____

Mural

What is a mural?

- A mural is a large picture on a wall.

- It is drawn or painted.

- It shows a scene, tells a story, or shows ideas about a topic.

- It is in a place where people can see it.

My Notes: _____

_____

Focus Question
How have new ideas changed communities?

How did the invention of television bring changes to communities?

Before Television	After Television

How Television Changed Communities

How do communities change and how do they stay the same? Write your answer.

_____

_____

_____

Study the Model

Fable

Read the Writing Model along with your teacher. Look for the lesson of the fable.

Model 1

The Prettiest Pet
by Justin Radnor

Porcupine and Peacock lived in the pet store. Every morning they got ready to show off for the store's customers.

Peacock spread her tail to show off its bright colors. "I'm the prettiest pet. How can anyone pass me by?" she thought to herself.

Porcupine was worried. He was not pretty. He was grey and had sharp quills. "No one will want me," he said sadly.

That day, a girl came to the store. She went over to Peacock. Porcupine sighed. Suddenly, the girl turned and continued down the row of animals. She stopped in front of Porcupine. Porcupine smiled and puffed his quills. Before long, he was on his way to his new home.

Lesson: Who you are inside is more important than how you look.

Study the Model

Fable

**Read the Writing Model along with your teacher.
Look for the lesson of the fable.**

Model 2

The Frog and The Grasshopper
by Alissa Walker

Frog and Grasshopper were the best jumpers in the swamp. They could jump high and far. They were always competing to see who was the better jumper. Frog liked to boast about his jumps. He told all the animals that he was a better jumper than Grasshopper. Grasshopper was tired of it. He challenged Frog to a contest.

"Whoever can jump the farthest over this log will win the contest," Grasshopper said.

Frog laughed. He knew he would beat Grasshopper.

"You jump first, Grasshopper," Frog said. Grasshopper smiled. He jumped over the log and landed.

Frog jumped over the log and landed in a huge mud puddle.

"You know what they say, Frog," Grasshopper laughed. "Look before you leap!"

Evaluation Rubric

Fable

Writing Trait	Goals	Yes	Needs work!	Now it's OK.
Organization	I name and describe my characters. My fable has a lesson.			
Ideas	My fable has a beginning, middle, and end. My fable has a problem and a solution.			
Voice	I use an appropriate voice for my audience.			
Word Choice	I use descriptive language to make my fable interesting. I use strong verbs to tell what happens.			
Sentence Fluency	My writing has rhythm and flow.			
Conventions	All the words are spelled correctly. I use correct punctuation. I use pronouns correctly.			

Peer Review

Fable

Read your partner's paper. Then finish each sentence.

1. The lesson of this fable is

_____

_____ .

2. An example of descriptive language that makes the fable interesting is

_____

_____ .

3. Some strong verbs that the writer might use are

_____

_____ .

Name of Reader _____

Pronouns That Show Ownership

You can use **pronouns** to show ownership.

my	his	its	their
your	her	our	

The cat ate **its** food.   We ate **our** food.

Fill in the blanks with pronouns that shows ownership.

1. That cap belongs to Jake.

That is _____ cap.

2. I own that book.

That is _____ book.

3. The girl has a blue shirt.

That is _____ blue shirt.

4. We live in that house.

That is _____ house.

5. Does that scooter belong to you?

Is that _____ scooter?

6. My brothers own that game.

That is _____ game.

Using Pronouns in Sentences

A **pronoun** has to match the noun it stands for.

- A plural noun takes a plural pronoun.

- A singular noun takes a singular pronoun.

- A feminine noun (for females) takes a feminine pronoun, and a masculine noun (for males) takes a masculine pronoun.

  Ricky walked the dog. **He** took it to the park.

  The **firefighters** went to the fire. **They** put it out.

  The **girl** kicked the ball. **She** made a goal.

Circle the correct pronouns.

1. Our class took a field trip to a museum. (We / He) went on a tour.

2. The museum had pictures from long ago. (They / It) showed the way our city looked back then.

3. One girl asked a question. (We / She) wanted to know if the old buildings were still in the city.

4. The tour guide asked our class whether (we / I) knew the answer.

5. I raised my hand. The tour guided nodded at (her / me).

6. I pointed to a building in one picture. I said that (they / it) was still on Main Street.

Taking Tests

Here is a question about *Kumak's Fish.*

Summarize the first part of *Kumak's Fish* from pages 5–9. Include the most important ideas and events in your summary.

How can you answer this question? First, look at the direction words.

Summarize means writing a paragraph that includes the most important ideas or events in the selection.

For example:

- The weather made it a good day for fishing.

- Kumak's wife, his wife's mother, and his children pulled on their warm clothes.

- Kumak packed them onto the sled.

- Kumak packed his uncle's amazing hooking stick that always caught many fish.

Think about the important ideas and events as you read the selection.

Taking Tests

Here is another question about *Kumak's Fish.*

Summarize the story from page 28 to the end. Include the most important ideas and events in your summary.

Important Events in Story

Use the events you wrote in the chart to help you write your summary.

_____

_____

_____

_____

My Weekly Planner

Week of _____

Theme Vocabulary	_____
Differentiated Vocabulary	_____
Comprehension Strategy and Skill	Strategy: _____ Skill: _____
Vocabulary Strategy	_____
Spelling Skill	_____
Fluency	Selection: _____
Writing and Language Arts	Writing form: _____
Grammar	Grammar skill: _____

Riddle

Read this riddle aloud.

Five Clues
by Sonny Cohen

Here is a riddle for you. Read the clues. Guess the answer.

As time goes by, don't expect us to stay the same. Some of us move around, and most of us get bigger. We all change and grow.

We can be grouped into big categories and smaller groups. Some of us have shells, some of us have hair, and some of us have feathers.

Some of us make food from sunlight and water. Some eat plants, and others hunt for food. We all need food and water.

We need to make more of our kind. Some of us send seeds into the wind, while others care for their babies. This is how we survive.

Who are we?

How well did you read? Circle your answer.

Answer Questions

Fill in the word skeletons by answering
the questions.

food, water, shelter, air

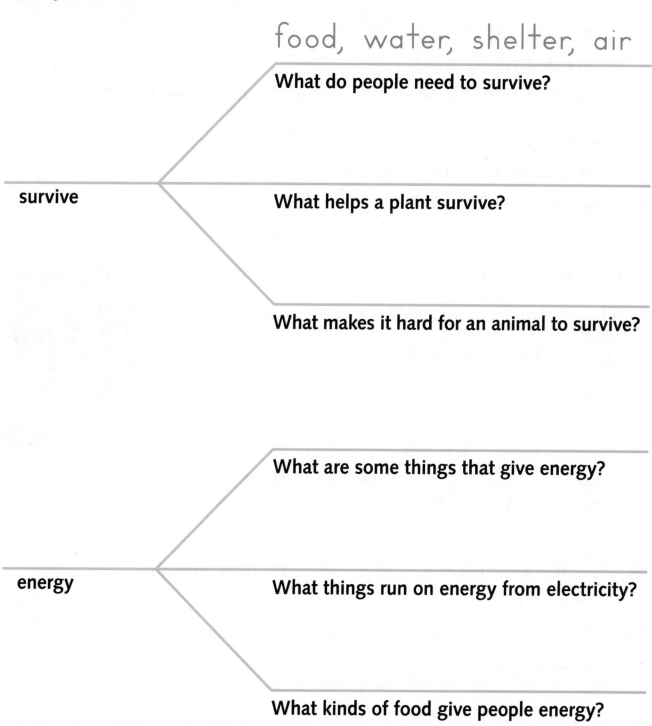

survive

What do people need to survive?

What helps a plant survive?

What makes it hard for an animal to survive?

energy

What are some things that give energy?

What things run on energy from electricity?

What kinds of food give people energy?

Word Roots

Words that share the same root have similar meanings.

survive–to be able to live
survival–staying alive
survivor–someone who lives through a terrible event

energy–something that is needed to do work
energize–to give energy to
energetic–strong and active

Complete the sentences.

1. All of the people on the plane were

   <u>survivors</u> of the crash.

2. Without water, plants cannot _____.

3. The _____ of so many animals
   after the fire amazed us.

4. You have to be _____ to play soccer.

5. A good breakfast will _____ you for
   the day.

6. A computer uses _____ to keep working.

Words Ending in -er

| after | never | paper | summer | were |
| better | under | winter | butter | different |

Fill in the crossword puzzles with spelling words.
Use the clues to help you.

1. Across: no longer sick
Down: opposite of *before*

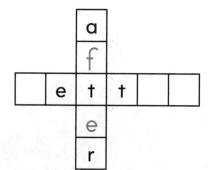

2. Across: the season after spring
Down: something to spread on bread

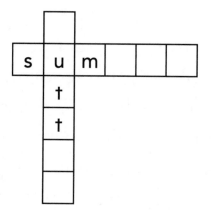

3. Across: not the same
Down: the season after fall

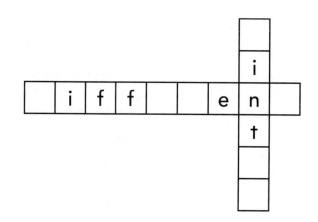

4. Across: below
Down: He was; they _____.

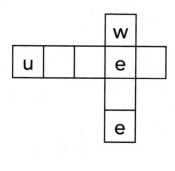

Make Inferences

To **make inferences**, you connect what you already know with what you read.

| What I Read | ➕ | What I Know | 🟰 | Inference: A new thought or idea |

Making inferences helps you understand what you are reading.

Read the text.

The seed from a pine tree sprouted in the spring. Soon a little seedling tree shot up from the forest floor. The summer was very dry. There was no rain for many days. The little seedling died. Another one will take its place in the spring.

Make an inference.

Why did the seedling die?   Possible answers:

What I Read		What I Know		Inference
There was no rain for many days.	➕	Plants need water to survive.	🟰	The seedling died because it didn't get enough water.

Read the text.

What is the world's largest mammal? The blue whale takes the prize. Everything about the blue whale is huge. This whale's heart is as big as a small car. Its tongue is so big that fifty people could stand on it.

Scientists think that the blue whale is the largest animal that has ever lived. The longest blue whale ever measured was 110 feet long. The heaviest weighed more than 150 tons. Of course, this is just a close guess. Scientists have weighed only parts of a dead blue whale to judge its weight.

Make an inference.

Why have scientists never weighed a whole blue whale?

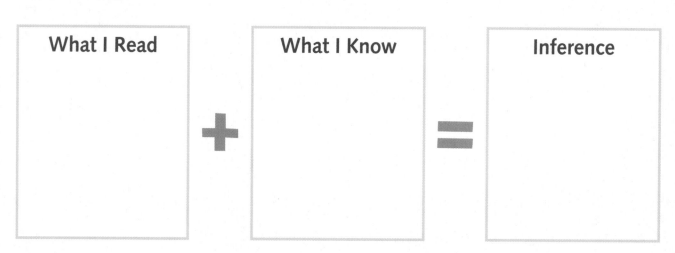

What I Read		What I Know		Inference
	+		=	

Determine Word Relationships

Several words can mean almost the same thing but have slightly different meanings.

The words *warm*, *hot*, and *boiling* all tell how hot something is.

← ─────────────────────────────────────── →

warm   hot   boiling

Writers choose words to show slightly different meanings.

| cold | chilly | freezing |

Write the words on the lines.

← ─────────────────────────────────────── →

chilly   cold   freezing

Write the words on the lines.

| lake | pond | ocean |

⟵──────────────────────────────────⟶

pond _____   _____   _____

| soaked | wet | damp |

⟵──────────────────────────────────⟶

_____   wet _____   _____

Sequence Events

Sequence is the order in which events happen. A sequence of events has a beginning, middle, and end.

Read the story. Think about the sequence.

In the spring, an apple tree grows new leaves and blossoms. Over the summer, the blossoms grow into apples. By autumn, the apples are ripe and ready to pick. Then the leaves change color and fall from the tree. Over the winter, the branches are bare, and the apple tree rests until the next spring.

Write the events from the story in the chart.

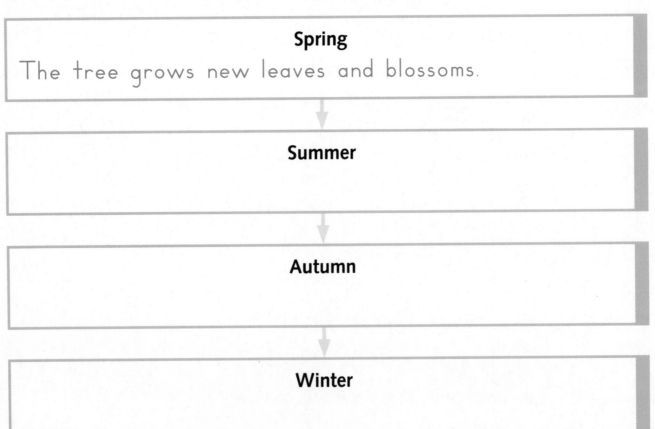

Spring

The tree grows new leaves and blossoms.

↓

Summer

↓

Autumn

↓

Winter

Unit 6, Project 1

Inquiry Planner

My Plan for Next Week

1. The Inquiry question is:

_____

_____

2. What information will I collect?

_____

3. How will I collect information?

☐ Books   ☐ Talking to people

☐ Other _____

4. Where will I collect information?

☐ My classroom   ☐ My school library
☐ At home   ☐ In my community

☐ Other _____

5. When will I collect information?

☐ During Self-Selected Reading time
☐ During Independent Practice time
☐ After school

Diagram

What is a diagram?

- A diagram is a picture of something, or a chart or web.

- A diagram uses labels to show important parts.

- A diagram can show how ideas are connected.

- A diagram can show the order of something.

How a Redwood Tree Grows

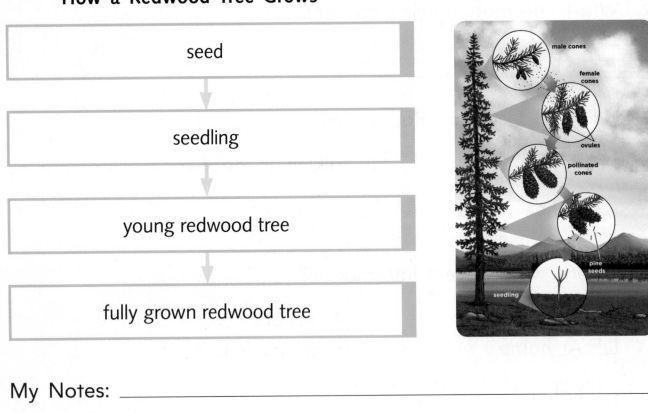

seed

↓

seedling

↓

young redwood tree

↓

fully grown redwood tree

male cones
female cones
ovules
pollinated cones
pine seeds
seedling

My Notes: _____

_____

Focus Question
What do living things have
in common?

What does the living thing that you read about
need to grow well? Make a list.

1. _____

2. _____

3. _____

4. _____

How do living things grow and change? Draw and
write your answer.

```



```

_____

_____

_____

Focus Question

How does a plant grow?

What changes do you see as a plant grows? Look at each picture. Tell how this plant changes.

An apple changes when _____.

Vegetables change when _____

_____.

Flowers change when _____.

My Weekly Planner

Week of _____

Theme Vocabulary	_____
Differentiated Vocabulary	_____
Comprehension Strategy and Skill	Strategy: _____ Skill: _____
Vocabulary Strategy	_____
Spelling Skill	_____
Fluency	Selection: _____
Writing and Language Arts	Writing form: _____
Grammar	Grammar skill: _____

Newspaper Article

Read this newspaper article aloud.

Go Garden
by Brooklyn Hollis

In 2009, First Lady Michelle Obama did something new at the White House. She started an organic garden. Organic gardening is fun and easy. For thousands of years, people have been able to grow plants without using harsh chemicals.

First, you will need some seeds. Choose what you like. Do you like strawberries? What about melons? Directions on the back of seed packets say when to plant the seeds. They tell you how deep to put the seeds into the soil and how far apart the plants should be.

Water the seeds a little bit every day. When the plants start to grow, you don't have to water them as much. You can stick your finger into the dirt. When the ground feels dry, water the plants. Fresh fruits and vegetables taste great!

How well did you read? Circle your answer.

88

Complete the Sentence

Complete each sentence. The first item has been done for you.

1. Ice **forms** when <u>water freezes</u> .

2. I carry an umbrella to **protect** _____

_____ .

3. One **problem** on our trip was that _____

_____ .

4. I practiced math **problems** _____

_____ .

5. In spring, buds begin to **form** _____

_____ .

6. Thick fur in the winter helps **protect** animals

_____ .

Related Words

Write a sentence using the two words.

1. Word: **form**   Related word: grow

   When a tree grows, it forms leaves

2. Word: **protect**   Related word: watch

   _____

   _____

3. Word: **problems**   Related word: difficult

   _____

   _____

4. Word: **protect**   Related word: lock

   _____

   _____

5. Word: **form**   Related word: make

   _____

   _____

Plurals

bells	names	boxes	wolves	was
days	babies	kisses	leaves	presents

Write the spelling word that goes with each clue.

1. They howl at the moon. _____

2. They are very young children. _____

3. There are seven in a week. _____

4. You get them on your birthday. _____

5. They make a sound when
someone rings them. _____

6. They grow on trees and are green. _____

7. They are touches you give with
your lips. _____

8. This word is the past tense of "is." _____

9. These words tell who you are. _____

10. You can keep things in them. _____

Summarize

To **summarize**:

- Decide which details are most important.

- Use your own words to write the summary.

Read the story. Look for important details.

A mother robin built her nest right outside my window. One day, the nest was full of blue eggs. Soon, the eggs hatched. The nest was full of hungry baby robins. The mother fed them worms. Before long, the little robins were flying off on their own. I felt like part of their family.

Write down three important details in the boxes. Then write a summary in the last box.

Important Idea	**Important Idea**	**Important Idea**
A mother robin built a nest and laid eggs in it.	The eggs hatched, and the nest was full of baby robins.	The baby robins flew out of the nest.

Summary

A mother robin built a nest and laid eggs in it. When the eggs hatched, the mother fed the babies until they could fly off on their own.

Read the story. Look for important details.

Every summer, sea turtles come onto Florida beaches. They make their nests and bury their eggs in the sand. Later, the baby turtles hatch and make their way to the ocean. Human beings can disturb this life cycle. Bright lights from houses and cars confuse the hatchlings. Plastic and other litter block the turtles' path to the sea. Cars can hurt or kill turtles on the beach. People in Florida are working together to make beaches safer for mother turtles and their babies. They are asking others to turn off bright lights and stop littering and driving on the beaches.

Write down three important details in the boxes. Then write a summary in the last box.

Important Idea	Important Idea	Important Idea

Summary

Similes

A **simile** is a statement in which the word *like* or *as* is used to compare two things. A simile helps readers picture something as they read.

Simile He jumps like a deer over the hurdles.

Meaning He runs fast and gracefully.

Write your own simile, comparing the two things in the photos. Explain the meaning of the simile.

Simile The clouds look as white and fluffy as sheep moving across the sky.

Meaning The clouds look like white sheep.

Write your own similes that compare two things.
Explain the meaning of each simile.

	Simile	
	Meaning	
	Simile	
	Meaning	
	Simile	
	Meaning	

Sequence Events

When you **sequence events**, you put them in the order in which they happened, from first to last. Putting events in order helps you understand a new idea.

Read the story. Fill in the sequence chart.

A Monarch butterfly goes through an amazing life cycle. It begins as an egg that the mother butterfly lays on a leaf or other food source. A caterpillar hatches from the egg. Next, the caterpillar forms a hard shell, or chrysalis, around itself. Inside the chrysalis, the caterpillar slowly turns into a butterfly. The butterfly breaks out of the chrysalis and unfolds its beautiful orange and black wings.

The mother butterfly lays an egg on a leaf.

↓

↓

↓

Think Back
Selection 2

Focus Question
How does a plant grow?

Think about the plants you read about. What do they have in common with other plants? Fill in the chart with your answers.

Plants I Read About	What They Have in Common	Other Plants
_____	_____	_____
_____	_____	_____
	_____	_____
	_____	

How do living things grow and change?

Write your answer.

_____

_____

_____

_____

_____

Focus Question

How do different kinds of animals grow?

How are young animals different from their parents?

Fill in the diagram.

Young Animals   **Parents**

98

Study the Model

Procedural: How-To

Read the Writing Model along with your teacher. Look for the steps of the how-to.

Model 1

Make a Home for Your Goldfish
by Michelle Garcia

Goldfish make great pets. You can make a nice place for them to live. Here's how!

What You Need:
- Soap
- Fish bowl
- Pebbles
- Plastic castle and plants
- Water

1. Wash the supplies with soap and water. Rinse them well.

2. Add pebbles to the fish bowl. They should be about two inches deep.

3. Goldfish need somewhere to hide. Add a plastic castle and plants.

4. Slowly fill the fish bowl with water.

5. Goldfish do not like noise. Place the fish bowl somewhere quiet and safe.

Study the Model

Procedural: How-To

Read the Writing Model along with your teacher. Look for the steps of the how-to.

Model 2

Grow Your Own Pumpkins
by Andy Chung

Have you ever wanted to grow your own pumpkins? All it takes is five easy steps.

What You Need:
- shovel
- yard stick
- 5 pumpkin seeds
- watering can

1. Soft seeds sprout faster, so start by soaking pumpkin seeds in water. Let them soak overnight.

2. Choose a sunny spot. Shovel soil into a mound that is three feet long.

3. Plant five seeds in the soil. Make sure they are at least six inches apart.

4. Cover the seeds with about an inch of soil.

5. Water the seeds gently. Keep the soil moist for several weeks. Then watch your pumpkins grow!

Evaluation Rubric

Procedural: How-To

Writing Trait	Goals	Yes	Needs work!	Now it's OK.
Organization	My steps are in the right order. I include all the important steps.			
Ideas	I explain how to do or make something. Each step clearly describes one part.			
Voice	The voice is right for my audience.			
Word Choice	I clearly describe items readers will need.			
Sentence Fluency	My sentences are smooth when I read them.			
Conventions	I use correct spelling and punctuation. I use adjectives correctly.			

Peer Review

Procedural: How-To

Read your partner's paper. Then finish each sentence.

1. This procedural explains how to

_____

_____

_____ .

2. Some describing words that the writer uses are

_____

_____

_____ .

3. Some examples of more specific words that the writer might use are

_____

_____

_____ .

Name of Reader _____

Adjectives for Color, Number, Size, and Shape

An **adjective** is a word that describes a noun. Adjectives can tell about

(color) (number) (size) (shape)

Adjectives come before the noun they describe, or they come after a verb.

The giraffe has a **long** neck.

The giraffe's neck is **long**.

Circle the adjective in each sentence. Write whether it describes color, number, size, or shape. The first item has been done for you.

1. An elephant has a (long) trunk. size

2. Two reptiles hung from the tree. _____

3. The frog has round spots on its skin. _____

Write an adjective that describes the noun.

4. The tree began as a _____ seed.

5. The bird is _____ .

Adjectives *a, an, the*

> The words *a, an,* and *the* are called **articles**. An article is an adjective that tells whether a noun is specific or not.
>
> - Use *a* or *an* before a non-specific singular noun. Use *an* if the noun begins with a vowel sound.
>
> - Use *the* before specific nouns.

Write the correct article at the end of each sentence. The first item has been done for you.

1. My family went to visit (an / the) aunt on her farm. <u>an</u>

2. It was in (a / the) spring. _____

3. We saw (a / the) cow with her new calf. _____

Write an article in the blank in each sentence. The first item has been done for you.

1. We went on <u>a</u> hike in the woods.

2. I picked up _____ acorn from the ground.

3. _____ acorn was small and green.

Taking Tests

What is a good summary of the information on page 8? (page 8)

(A) A frightened turtle pulls its head into its shell.

(B) Some plants move to face the sun.

(C) Animals can run, swim, or fly.

(D) Most living things can move by themselves.

What is the question asking for? A summary of the information on the page.

- Is the sentence about the turtle a summary of the information on the page? No, it is just a detail.

- Is the sentence about plants a good summary? No, it doesn't mention animals.

- Is the sentence about animals a good summary? No, it doesn't mention plants.

- Is the sentence about living things moving by themselves a good summary? Yes, it covers animals and plants and sums up the information on the page.

Look at the questions on the next page.

Taking Tests

Fill in the circle for the right answer to each question.

1. **How would you find the answer to the question: Are reptiles warm-blooded?** (page 11)

   Ⓐ Look on the chart under *reptiles* and *Are warm-blooded.*
   Ⓑ Look on the chart under *reptiles* and *mammals.*
   Ⓒ Read the text.
   Ⓓ Look at the picture of the snake.

2. **What can you infer about frogs?** (page 17)

   Ⓐ An adult frog is funny looking.
   Ⓑ Tadpoles don't have legs.
   Ⓒ Frog babies look nothing like frog adults.
   Ⓓ Many animals hatch from eggs.

3. **What is the sequence of the life cycle of a female beetle?** (page 20)

   Ⓐ pupa, egg, larva, adult
   Ⓑ adult, egg, pupa, larva
   Ⓒ egg, larva, pupa, adult
   Ⓓ egg, adult, pupa, larva

4. **Which statement is an opinion?** (pages 24–26)

   Ⓐ Gorillas live in large family groups.
   Ⓑ Bats like to eat frogs.
   Ⓒ A small moose is called a calf.
   Ⓓ Bats are ugly animals.

My Weekly Planner

Week of _____

Theme Vocabulary	_____
Differentiated Vocabulary	_____
Comprehension Strategy and Skill	Strategy: _____ Skill: _____
Vocabulary Strategy	_____
Spelling Skill	_____
Fluency	Selection: _____
Writing and Language Arts	Writing form: _____
Grammar	Grammar skill: _____

Dialogue

Read this dialogue aloud.

Growing Up

by Dana Mann

Kangaroo: My story is pretty unusual. When I was born, I was no bigger than a human child's thumb. My eyes were shut tight. I had to crawl a long way to find my mother's pouch. I stayed in there until I got much bigger.

Frog: Here's my story. When I was born, I had millions of siblings. We lived in water. We had heads and tails that we used for swimming. Then I grew front and back legs. Now I live on land.

Moth: Wait until you hear my story! When I was born, I looked like a worm with feet. All day long, I ate leaves. Then I spun a cover and wrapped myself up tight. When I came out, I was much different. I had wings and I could fly!

How well did you read? Circle your answer.

Word Map

Fill in the word map for the word *single*.

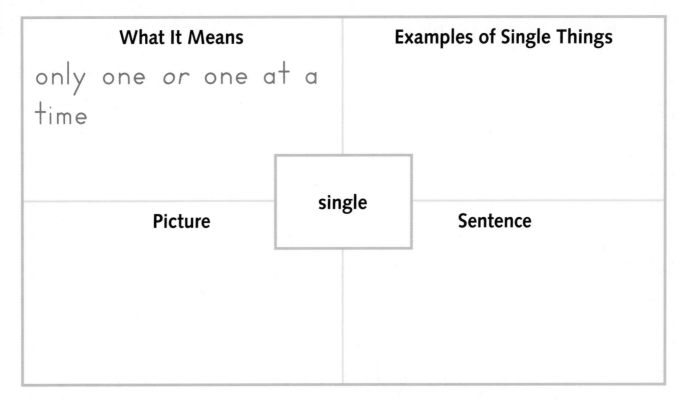

What It Means	Examples of Single Things
only one *or* one at a time	
Picture	**Sentence**

single

Fill in the word map for the word *shuffle*.

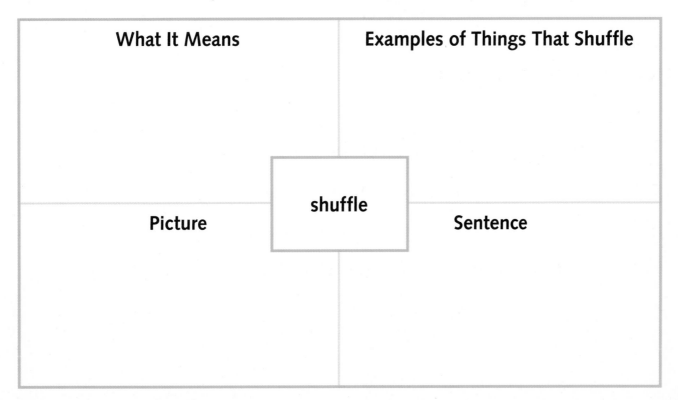

What It Means	Examples of Things That Shuffle
Picture	**Sentence**

shuffle

Sentence Completions

Write the word *single* or *shuffled* in each blank.

1. We lost the game by a _____ point.

2. I _____ my feet to the music.

3. The penguins _____ across the ice.

4. I ate so much that I couldn't eat a _____ bite of dessert.

5. After the long race, the tired runners _____ off the field.

6. In my room, I have a _____ bed.

7. The morning after my slumber party, I _____ to the kitchen for waffles.

8. When the baby smiled, she showed a _____ new tooth.

Adding -ed and -ing

wanted	missed	hugging	eating	swimming
liked	clapped	sitting	taking	getting

Write the -ed form of each word. Fill in the letters to be added.

1. want + e___ d___ = wanted

2. miss + _____ _____ = _____

3. like + _____ = _____

4. clap + _____ _____ _____ = _____

Write the -ing form of each word. Fill in the letters to be added or subtracted.

5. hug + g___ i___ n___ g___ = hugging

6. eat + _____ _____ _____ = _____

7. sit + _____ _____ _____ _____ = _____

8. take − _____ + _____ _____ _____ = _____

9. get + _____ _____ _____ _____ = _____

10. swim + _____ _____ _____ _____ = _____

111

Make Connections

| Connect to something you have done. | Connect to something you have read about. | Connect to something you learned about on TV. |

Read the paragraph.

Hannah is learning to play basketball. Her parents hung a basketball hoop on the garage so that she could practice. Every day, Hannah tries to shoot 25 baskets. Sometimes she makes 5 baskets. Sometimes she makes 10. When basketball season begins, Hannah will join a team.

Make connections to the text. Write your connections.

In the Text	This Reminds Me of
Hannah is learning to play basketball. Her parents hung a basketball hoop on the garage.	In the book we read about soccer, the boy had his own soccer ball and net in his backyard.

Connection
- ⊗ Text
- ○ Self
- ○ World

Read the paragraph.

A mother polar bear digs a cave in a large snowdrift. Over the winter, she has her cubs. When they are born, the cubs are smaller than human babies. They are about the size of rats. They weigh a bit more than a pound each. The mother and babies stay in the cave through the winter. The mother feeds them and takes care of them. By spring, the cubs are larger. They leave the cave with their mother. They are ready for adventures.

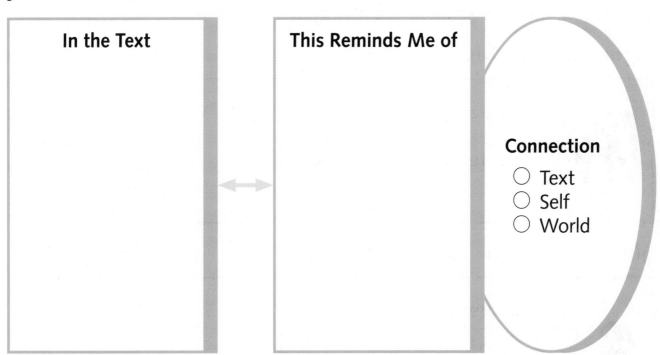

Make connections to the text. Write down your connections.

In the Text	This Reminds Me of

Connection
- ○ Text
- ○ Self
- ○ World

Thesaurus

A **thesaurus** is a book that contains synonyms, or words that have similar meanings.

A thesaurus lists words in ABC order. Each entry word is followed by synonyms.

> **gigantic**, *adjective:* **big, huge, large**

> **glance**, *verb:* **look, see**

Read the thesaurus entries. Write one sentence using the word and one sentence using a synonym.

gigantic, *adjective:* big, huge, large

Sentence: The elephant was gigantic.

Sentence with synonym: The elephant was huge.

glance, *verb:* look, see

Sentence : Just glance at the clock from time to time.

Sentence with synonym: Just look at the clock from time to time.

Read the sentence describing each picture. Then use the thesaurus entry to help you revise the sentence with a synonym.

1. **horrible**, *adjective:* awful, frightening, ugly

The lizard had a **horrible** face.

Sentence with synonym:

2. **construct**, *verb:* build, make, form

Beavers **construct** dams in ponds.

Sentence with synonym:

3. **predator**, *noun:* foe, attacker, enemy

The shark is the **predator** of many ocean fish.

Sentence with synonym:

Before and After Reading

Read the statements about *The Emperor's Egg.*
Write a Y for *yes.* Write an N for *no.*

Before	The Emperor's Egg	After
	This story probably takes place near the South Pole.	
	The main character is a man who is king, or emperor, of a country.	
	Penguin babies hatch from eggs.	
	Only the mother penguin takes care of the baby penguin.	
	Penguins live in big groups to protect themselves from their cold environment.	

Setting

The **setting** of a story tells

- where and when the story takes place

Read the story. Answer the questions about the setting.

Dad promised us an adventure on our summer vacation. The first afternoon, Dad looked at a map of Florida.

"Let's go to Mosquito Lagoon," he said. "It has a great nature trail."

It didn't sound like a friendly place, but we all piled in the car.

When we arrived, no one was in the parking lot. Dad led the way to the nature trail. Thick trees and bushes surrounded it. Suddenly, my little brother screamed. He had walked into a spider web.

Then my mom started screaming. She was batting away a swarm of mosquitoes. Soon, the mosquitoes attacked us like a hungry army. We ran to the car.

"That was some adventure, Dad!" I said.

1. Where does the story take place?

   The story takes place <u>in Florida on a nature trail</u>.

2. When does the story take place?

   The story takes place _____.

Read and Respond

Think about what you read in *The Emperor's Egg.*
Then answer these questions. The first one has
been done for you.

1. **What was the most surprising thing you learned
about Emperor penguins?**

   I thought it amazing that a male
   Emperor penguin can stand in the
   cold for two whole months! He
   can't hunt, play, or rest. He can
   just take care of his egg.

2. **Would you like to visit Antarctica and see the
penguins?**

   _____

   _____

3. **What did you learn about animal survival from
this book?**

   _____

   _____

   _____

Distinguish Facts and Opinions

A reader needs to know how to tell the difference between a **fact** and an **opinion**.

- A **fact** is information that can be proved.

- An **opinion** is a personal idea about something.

Read each sentence. Write the word *fact* or *opinion* next to each one. Tell how you know.

Sentence	Fact or Opinion?	How Do You Know?
1. A snake is a reptile.	fact	I can check the statement in a science book.
2. I think that snakes are gross.		
3. Spiders have eight legs.		
4. Redwoods are the largest trees.		
5. I believe that all people should have pets.		

Unit 6, Project 2

Inquiry Planner

My Plan for Next Week

1. The Inquiry question is:

   _____

   _____

2. What information will I collect?

   _____

3. How will I collect information?

   ☐ Books   ☐ Talking to people

   ☐ Other _____

4. Where will I collect information?

   ☐ My classroom   ☐ My school library
   ☐ At home   ☐ In my community

   ☐ Other _____

5. When will I collect information?

   ☐ During Self-Selected Reading time
   ☐ During Independent Practice time
   ☐ After school

Think Back
Selection 3

Focus Question
How do different kinds of animals grow?

Think about the animal you read about. How does the animal change as it grows? Write your answer.

_____

_____

_____

_____

How do living things grow and change?

Draw and write your answer.

_____

_____

Focus Question
What do animals learn as they grow?

How do young animals know what to eat?
How do they learn to survive? Write about
each of the pictures.

_____

_____

_____

_____

_____

_____

_____

_____

_____

_____

My Weekly Planner

Week of _____

Theme Vocabulary	_____
Differentiated Vocabulary	_____
Comprehension Strategy and Skill	Strategy: _____ Skill: _____
Vocabulary Strategy	_____
Spelling Skill	_____
Fluency	Selection: _____
Writing and Language Arts	Writing form: _____
Grammar	Grammar skill: _____

Poem

Read this poem aloud.

How We Learn
by Lee Clifford

We watch the bigger ones, our
mothers, fathers, older sisters,
and brothers.
We watch what they do, and we
copy them.
We copy them, but we are clumsy.
We can't do things well.
We like to play, and playing is how we practice.
We get bigger and better, and we are able
to do more.
Some day, other little ones will watch what we do.

They will watch what we do and copy us.
They will be clumsy, but we will help them.
They will play and won't realize that play is practice.
They will get bigger and better. And then they will
be able to do more.
Some day, other little ones will watch them.

How well did you read? Circle your answer.

Examples

Examples can help you understand the meaning of a word.

Is a twin a **single** baby? <u>no</u>

Write *yes* or *no* to answer each example question.

1. Do runners **shuffle** along during a race? <u>no</u>

2. Does a flashlight get its **energy** from a battery? _____

3. Does a home help you **survive**? _____

4. Does a tree **form** leaves on its branches? _____

5. Is lack of food a **problem** in some places? _____

6. Do firefighters help **protect** a community? _____

7. Can you turn off the **energy** from the sun? _____

8. Can a polar bear **survive** a snowstorm? _____

Connect Words

survive	energy	form	protect
problems	single	shuffle	

Answer each question in a sentence. Use two vocabulary words in your answer.

1. When might you have a **problem** with **energy**?

If the power went out, I would have a problem with energy.

2. Can a **single** animal **survive** as well as a group of animals?

_____

_____

3. How do plants use **energy** to **form** seeds?

_____

Look at the picture. Using vocabulary words, write a sentence about what you see.

_____

Comparative Endings -*er*, -*est*

louder	higher	nicer	biggest	other
coldest	tallest	easier	funniest	another

Complete the spelling word in each sentence.

1. It was the cold e s t winter in history.

2. I saw the fun _____ movie ever.

3. I turned the music up loud _____.

4. This puzzle was easi _____ than the last one.

5. I made the big _____ sandwich ever!

6. I want _____ other cookie.

7. There is nice _____ weather in spring than in winter.

8. Bill is the tall _____ student in the class.

9. Math is taught in the oth _____ classroom.

10. The chairs are high _____ in second grade than in first grade.

Ask and Answer Questions

- **Ask**: What question do I have about what I read?

- **Look** for clues in the text to answer the question.

- **Use** what you already know.

- **Answer** your question.

Read. Write a question. Then fill in the chart.

A young Canada goose is called a gosling. It is born in the spring, with fuzzy feathers like a baby duck. It can swim right away. By the fall, its flight feathers have grown in. 40–70 days after birth, the young goose is ready for a long flight with its family.

Ask: *What long flight will the young goose be taking?*

Information from Text	What You Already Know	Answer the Question
By fall, the flight feathers have grown in.	Many birds fly south for the winter.	A young goose will fly south for the winter.

Read. Write a question. Then fill in the chart.

Deena's family was camping out. Sitting by the campfire, Deena's dad talked about the bears that sometimes came through the woods. He told Deena that the bears were wild and often hungry. After dinner, Deena's mother put all of their food away so that bears couldn't smell it.

Deena found half a sandwich in her backpack. She thought about the hungry bears. Maybe the sandwich would feed them. Deena took the sandwich outside. Her father saw her just in time.

"No, Deena," he said. "Never feed a hungry bear!"

Ask: _____

Information from Text	What You Already Know	Answer the Question

Use Multiple Strategies

Words can relate to each other in different ways. We choose a word based on its special meaning.

Write the words in order in the boxes.

1. hot

burning

icy

lukewarm

Most cold

icy
lukewarm
hot
burning

Least cold

2. large

tiny

huge

little

Smallest

Biggest

3. sky blue

white

navy blue

black

Darkest

Lightest

130

A **thesaurus** is a book that contains synonyms, or words that have similar meanings.

A thesaurus lists words in ABC order. Each entry word is followed by synonyms.

run, *verb:* hurry, race

walk, *verb:* hike, shuffle, step

Circle synonyms for *walk* and *run.* Then write the words in order in the boxes.

(hurry)

run

walk

(shuffle)

Fastest

| |
| |
| |
| |

Slowest

Read the thesaurus entry. Write one sentence using a synonym.

walk, *verb:* hike, shuffle, step

_____

_____

Before and After Reading

Read the sentences. Do you agree or disagree?

1	2	3	4
Agree	Mostly Agree	Mostly Disagree	Disagree

Before you read, write a number from this scale on the line before the statement. After you read, write a number from this scale on the line after the statement.

Before	The River Otters	After
_____	**1.** River otters are good runners and good swimmers.	_____
_____	**2.** You don't have to be the strongest or fastest to be the cleverest otter.	_____
_____	**3.** You can learn important lessons through playing.	_____

Before	Gosling School	After
_____	**1.** Ducks dive underwater for food.	_____
_____	**2.** Baby ducks can't learn to fly until they're older.	_____
_____	**3.** Some young animals have to try things their way.	_____

Lion Pride		
Before		**After**
———	**1.** Only male lions hunt for food.	———
———	**2.** Lions don't have to be afraid of any animals.	———
———	**3.** Baby lions learn lessons from their parents.	———

The Meerkat Pack		
Before		**After**
———	**1.** Meerkats can stand on two legs.	———
———	**2.** A young meerkat gets better at something by practicing.	———
———	**3.** There is safety in numbers in the wild.	———

Distinguish Fact and Opinion

Learn to tell the difference between a fact and an opinion.

- A fact is a piece of information that can be proved.

- An opinion is a statement that someone believes or thinks.

A **fact** has information that you can check in a book or other source to learn whether it is true.	An **opinion** often has signal words such as "I believe," "I think," or "In my opinion."

Read each sentence. Write the word *fact* or *opinion* next to each one. Then write how you know.

Sentence	Fact or Opinion?	How Do I Know?
1. I think penguins are the cutest animals.	opinion	The sentence starts with "I think."
2. Frogs are amphibians.		
3. Soft feathers help keep an albatross chick warm.		
4. In my opinion, we should protect all animals.		

Book of Illustrations

What is a book of illustrations?

- It shows pictures about an idea, concept, or theme.

- It uses text and labels where needed.

- It has a cover with a title and an author.

My Notes: _____

_____

_____

Focus Question
What do animals learn as they grow?

What does the animal that you read about learn as it grows? What does it learn about?

Lesson

Lesson

Lessons My Animal Learned

Lesson

Lesson

How do living things grow and change?
Write your answer.

_____

_____

_____

_____

Study the Model

Persuasive Poster

Read the Writing Model along with your teacher. Look for facts and opinions in the poster.

Summer Fun!

You won't want to miss this!
Running Deer Summer Camp

July 6 – July 17

Come to the best camp in town!
Make new friends!

Enjoy these fun activities:

- Swimming
- Fishing
- Kayaking
- Bird Watching

Kids love Running Deer Summer Camp. You will too!

Study the Model

Persuasive Letter

Read the Writing Model along with your teacher. Look for facts and opinions in the letter.

April 30, 2011

Dear Mr. Jackson,

I loved your book about snakes! I think you should write one about frogs. Frogs would be a great topic for a book.

For one thing, kids love looking at pictures. Frogs can be a lot of different colors. If you include some amazing photographs, then every kid would read your book.

Kids also love interesting facts, and frogs are *really* interesting! They start out as tadpoles. They can jump really far. They can breathe through their skin.

If you write a book about frogs, a lot of kids would read it. Since you are my favorite author, I know you would write a great book.

Sincerely,

Darryl Porter

Evaluation Rubric

Persuasive Writing

Writing Trait	Goals	Yes	Needs work!	Now it's OK.
Organization	The order of my ideas makes sense.			
Ideas	I state my opinion. I use facts and opinions to persuade.			
Voice	My writing sounds like me when I read it aloud.			
Word Choice	I use strong persuasive words.			
Sentence Fluency	I use different kinds of sentences.			
Conventions	All the words are spelled correctly. I use correct punctuation. I use adjectives and adverbs correctly.			

Peer Review

Persuasive Writing

Read your partner's paper. Then finish each sentence.

1. The writer is trying to persuade the reader to

   _____

   _____

   _____ .

2. Some examples of opinions in the letter or poster are

   _____

   _____

   _____ .

3. The writer might use strong persuasive words like

   _____

   _____

   _____ .

Name of Reader _____

Adjectives That Compare

to compare two people, places, or things:	add -er to most one-syllable adjectives:
	smaller, taller, greener, longer
to compare three or more people, places, or things:	add -est to most one-syllable adjectives:
	slowest, biggest, fastest, smartest

Circle the correct adjective that compares something in each sentence. Then write the word. The first item has been done for you.

1. The cheetah is the (faster / (fastest)) of all land animals. <u>fastest</u>

2. A hippo is (smaller / smallest) than an elephant.

   _____

3. A bird is (bigger / biggest) than a worm.

   _____

4. Brad is the (taller / tallest) of my three brothers.

   _____

Adverbs

An **adverb** describes a verb. **Adverbs** can tell how, when, or where something happens.

how	when	where
loudly	yesterday	everywhere
quickly	soon	here
silently	later	there

Circle the adverb in each sentence. Write whether it tells how, when, or where. The first item has been done for you.

1. (Yesterday), I went to our town's park. <u>when</u>

2. I quickly ran to the playground. _____

3. I saw my friend there.

4. I called out his name loudly. _____

5. He answered back happily. _____

Taking Tests

Here is a question about *The Emperor's Egg.*

Describe the sequence of events that take place on pages 10–16 of *The Emperor's Egg.* Include the most important events in correct order.

How can you answer this question? First, look at the direction words.

Describe the sequence of events means tell about the events in the order in which they took place. (The story doesn't always tell about the events in order.) *Include the most important events* means tell only the most important things that happened, not every detail. For example:

- The female penguin lays an egg.

- She waddles off to the sea.

- The father is left to take care of the egg.

- The father has to stay with the egg for two whole months.

Taking Tests

Here is another question about *The Emperor's Egg*.

Describe the sequence of events that take place on pages 23–28 of *The Emperor's Egg*. Include the most important events in the order in which they take place.

Sequence of Important Events
1.
2.
3.
4.

Use the sequence of events to write a paragraph about the story.

_____

_____

_____

My Weekly Planner

Week of _____

Theme Vocabulary	_____
Differentiated Vocabulary	_____
Comprehension Strategy and Skill	Strategy: _____ Skill: _____
Vocabulary Strategy	_____
Spelling Skill	_____
Fluency	Selection: _____
Writing and Language Arts	Writing form: _____
Grammar	Grammar skill: _____

Poem

Read this poem aloud.

We, the People
by Cy Wilson

We, the people, came together
More than 200 years ago.
We were common people,
Not a group of princes and kings.
We agreed to live together peacefully
On this land.

We agreed to respect the laws
That we made.
We joined together to protect ourselves
From enemies who might try to hurt us.
We joined together because together
We can find ways to make our lives better.
But we also like to live freely
Without too many rules.

We came together so we could live this way.
This is the way of life we want for our children
And our children's children.

How well did you read? Circle your answer.

Idea Completion

government	elect	taxes

Choose one of the vocabulary words to complete each sentence. One example has been done for you.

1. The people of the United States vote to

   <u>elect</u>_____ leaders, such as the President.

2. The state gathers _____ to support community services, such as schools.

3. The leaders in the city _____ meet at City Hall.

4. People in our state will _____ someone to be the governor.

5. People pay _____ when they buy things.

6. A _____ elected by the people makes the laws.

Use Word Web

Fill in the word web with things our government does. One example has been done for you.

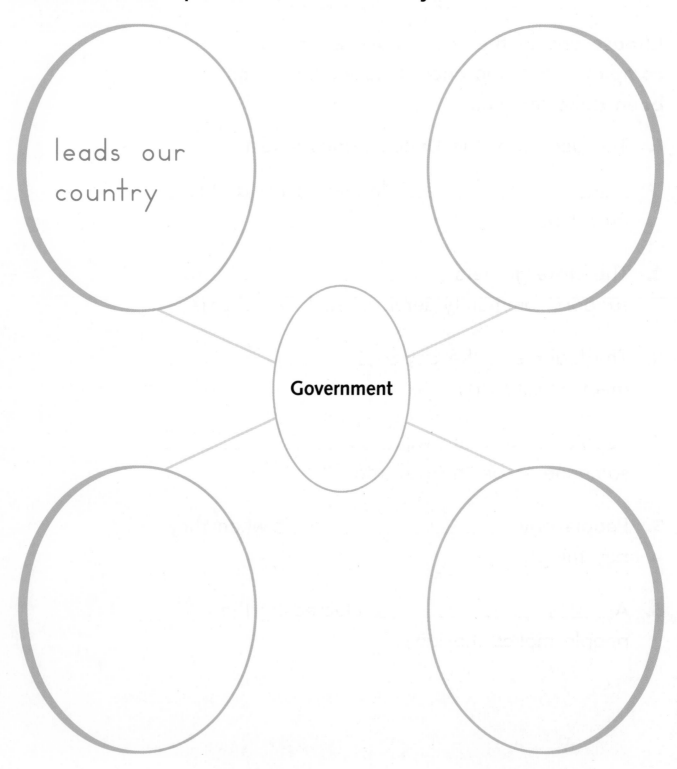

leads our country

Government

Words with *r*-Controlled Vowels

You hear the same vowel sound in words
containing the letters *ear*, *eer*, and *ere*.

year	clear	here	cheer	great
fear	beard	deer	steer	hurt

**Sort the spelling words. Write them on the lines.
Circle the letters that spell the vowel sound.**

ear

y(ear) _____

_____

_____

_____

eer

_____

_____

_____

ere

_____

Frequently Misspelled

_____

_____

Write the spelling word that completes each sentence.

1. The _____ ran through the woods.

2. I will stay _____ at home.

Visualize

When you **visualize**, you make a picture in your mind.

To visualize, you

• use what you read and what you know

Read the story. Make pictures in your mind.

Every year, the town of Ridgewood has a big fair. The fair is held at the town park. The people in the community walk around and talk to their neighbors. There are tables where people buy food and drinks. People buy hamburgers, hot dogs, and tacos. There are all kinds of rides for children. The pony rides are a favorite. There are also rides, such as a merry-go-round and a Ferris wheel. The fair is fun for everyone.

What I Read	Pictures in My Mind
Ridgewood has a big fair at the town park. People walk around and talk to their neighbors.	I see a big crowd of people having fun. It is a sunny day, and everyone is enjoying the fair.

Read the story. Create pictures in your mind.

On the Fourth of July, the town of Red Hook has a parade. The mayor is at the front of the parade. He rides in an open car. A marching band comes next. The band plays a loud song, and people clap along. There are always a lot of fire engines in the parade. The firefighters wave to the people lining the streets. At the end of the parade come the clowns. They make everyone laugh and cheer.

What I Read	Pictures in My Mind

Idioms

An **idiom** is a phrase whose meaning is different from that of the individual words.

The test was <u>a piece of cake</u>. I got an A.

What does the idiom mean? <u>very easy</u>

Read the sentence. Then write the meaning of the idiom.

We needed umbrellas because it was <u>raining cats and dogs</u>.

What does the idiom mean?

<u>The rain was coming down</u>
<u>very hard.</u>

Read each sentence. Then write the meaning of the idiom.

1. My mom <u>chewed me out</u> when she saw my dirty clothes.

   What is the meaning of the idiom?

_____

_____

2. At yesterday's soccer game, the final goal was made just <u>in the nick of time</u>.

   What is the meaning of the idiom?

_____

_____

3. Marsha's <u>eyes were bigger than her stomach</u>, so she couldn't eat all of the food on her plate.

   What is the meaning of the idiom?

_____

_____

Draw Conclusions

To **draw conclusions**:

- use facts and details from the text

- use what you already know

Read the story. Then fill in the chart.

Kim was going to the grocery store with her mother. Their neighbor, Mr. Beal, was pulling out of his garage. Suddenly, Mr. Beal stopped his car and got out. He went back inside the house.

"Why did Mr. Beal go back inside?" Kim asked.

"He's got his gym bag now," Mom said.

Why did Mr. Beal go back inside after he left?

Information from Text	What I Know
Mr. Beal ran back inside.	

Conclusion

Unit 7, Project 1

Inquiry Planner

My Plan for Next Week

1. The Inquiry question is:

_____

_____

2. What information will I collect?

_____

3. How will I collect information?

☐ Books   ☐ Talking to people

☐ Other _____

4. Where will I collect information?

☐ My classroom   ☐ My school library
☐ At home   ☐ In my community

☐ Other _____

5. When will I collect information?

☐ During Self-Selected Reading time
☐ During Independent Practice time
☐ After school

Prepare to Present

Class Inquiry Question: _____

_____

Circle one for each.

1. What does your research show?

2. How will you share your findings?

steps in a process

relationships

cause and effect

a story

how something works

| Diagram |
| Book of Illustrations |

| Diagram |

| Chart or Diagram |
| Skit |
| Puppet Show |
| Book of Illustrations |

| Picture Book   Skit |
| Puppet Show |

| Diagram   Mural |
| Picture Book |

Focus Question
What is a government?

What did you learn about government in this selection? Write your ideas.

_____

_____

_____

_____

What role does government play in your community?

Write your answer.

_____

_____

Focus Question
Where can I see government in action in my community?

Look at the photos. What roles does the government play in these places? Write your ideas.

_____

_____

_____

_____

_____

_____

My Weekly Planner

Week of _____

Theme Vocabulary	_____
Differentiated Vocabulary	_____
Comprehension Strategy and Skill	Strategy: _____ Skill: _____
Vocabulary Strategy	_____
Spelling Skill	_____
Fluency	Selection: _____
Writing and Language Arts	Writing form: _____
Grammar	Grammar skill: _____

Dialogue

Read this dialogue aloud.

Government You Can See
by Corey Winn

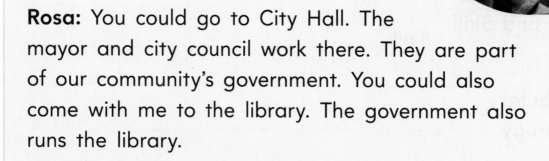

Kent: I need help with my homework. Do you know how I can find examples of government in our community? I'm not sure where to look.

Rosa: You could go to City Hall. The mayor and city council work there. They are part of our community's government. You could also come with me to the library. The government also runs the library.

Curtis: I have an idea! You could come to the park with me. The community government takes care of it. If we ride the bus to the park, we would be using another government service.

Tasha: You could stay right here at school. The government runs public schools. So, you have your first example right here!

How well did you read? Circle your answer.

Opinion Chart

Read each issue in the middle column. Put a check mark in the left column if you agree or in the right column if you don't agree. Add two issues of your own.

Agree	Issues	Don't Agree
	People who litter should be fined.	
	The laws should be the same for bikers and drivers.	
	City buses should be free.	
	Alligators make fine pets.	
	No one should have to go hungry in our country.	

Word Map

Fill in the chart for the word *agree.* Tell what the word means. Draw a picture of two friends agreeing. Then write a sentence about the picture.

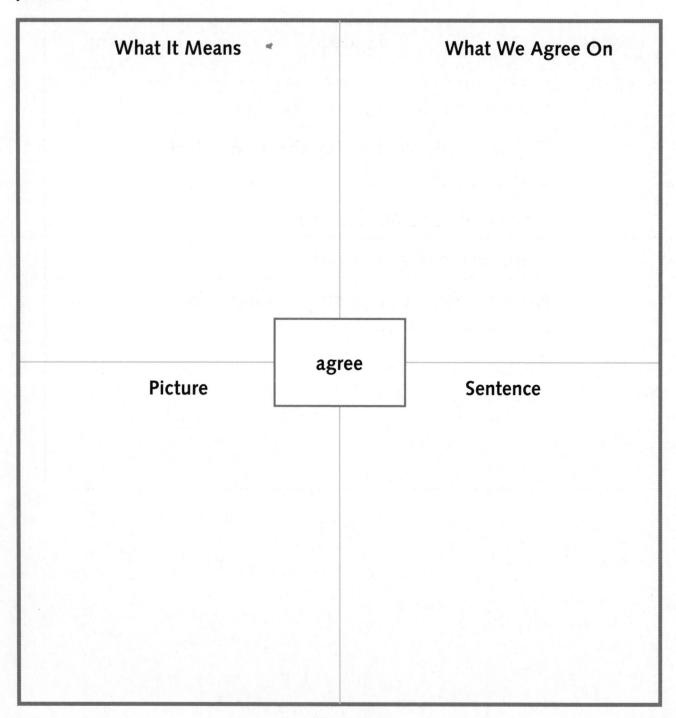

What It Means

What We Agree On

agree

Picture

Sentence

Contractions

When we speak, we often use a **contraction**, a word shortened from two words.

I'm	he'd	didn't	that's	they're
we'll	it's	can't	you're	don't

Write the contraction for each set of words.
Then draw a line through each letter that was taken out to make the contraction.

1. I + ~~a~~m = I'm _____

2. can + not = _____

3. did + not = _____

4. we + will = _____

5. it + is = _____

6. that + is = _____

7. they + are = _____

8. you + are = _____

9. do + not = _____

Determine Important Information

When you **determine important information**, you

- think about what the text is mostly about
- decide which information is most important to the main idea
- decide which information is interesting but not important

Read the story and look for the most important information. Then fill in the chart.

Last weekend our community had a tree-planting day. The goal was to plant 500 trees. We planted a tree in our yard. We bought the tree at a nursery.

The town council counted every tree that was planted. My uncle is on the town council. Our community planted 504 trees!

Important	Our community had a tree-planting day. The goal was to plant 500 trees. The town council kept count.
Not Important	We bought the tree at a nursery. My uncle is on the town council.

Read the story and look for the most important information. Then fill in the chart.

Every summer, our town has a reading marathon. The goal is to read twenty books during the summer. My friend and I signed up at the library. We took out some books that looked interesting.

On the last day, I read one whole book. I met the goal and won a medal!

Important	
Not Important	

Classify Words

When you **classify** words, you put the words into groups.

**Read the words. Put them in the right group.
Add an example to each group.**

| bus | library | train |
| bicycle | ball field | mountains |

Ways to Travel	Places to Go
bus	ball field
bicycle	library
train	mountains
airplane	skating rink

Read the words. Put them in the right group.
Add an example to each group.

mayor	recycling center	firefighters	library
paramedics	police station	Navy nurse	town hall

Government Workers	Government Buildings

Identify Main Idea and Details

The **main idea** is what a text is mostly about. **Details** tell more about the main idea.

Ask: *What is this story mostly about?*

Ask: *What details tell me more about the main idea?*

Read the story. Fill in the chart.

Communities have workers who help in an emergency. Firefighters rush to put out fires and save people. Paramedics help people with medical emergencies. Animal control workers help if a wild animal puts people in danger. These workers make a community a safe place to live.

MAIN IDEA	DETAILS
	Firefighters put out fires and save people.

168

Focus Question
Where can I see government in action in my community?

How has local government made a difference for the people in the story you read? Write your ideas.

Problem	
Solution	

What role does the government play in your community?

Write your answer.

_____

_____

_____

Focus Question

How does a local government help make a good community?

Look at these pictures. How do these things make a community a good place to live? Write your answers on the lines.

_____

_____

_____

Study the Model

Quatrain

Read the Writing Model along with your teacher. Look for the rhymes of the quatrain.

Model 1

Sleigh Ride
by Amy Wilson

On a cold and wintry day,
Liz and her sisters went out to play.
Once they'd finished their sleigh ride,
Liz and her sisters came inside.

The American Flag
by Keith Sender

A banner filled with stripes and stars
in the mighty wind is blowing.
Signifying what is ours:
a great nation ever growing.

Study the Model

Shape Poem

Read the Writing Model along with your teacher. Look for the shape of the poem.

Sunshine
by Lisa Thompson

Sun

Shining brightly,

like a ball of fire in the sky.

Giving light to all the earth.

Showering us

With warmth.

Shine

172

Evaluation Rubric

Quatrain and Shape Poems

Writing Trait	Goals	Yes	Needs work!	Now it's OK.
Organization	My quatrain has four lines. My shape poem's shape tells about my topic.			
Ideas	My poem expresses feelings or ideas.			
Voice	My poem sounds like me when I read it aloud.			
Word Choice	My quatrain has the correct rhyme scheme.			
Sentence Fluency	The lines of my poem have rhythm and flow.			
Conventions	I use correct spelling punctuation and capital letters.			

Peer Review

Quatrain and Shape Poems

Read your partner's poem. Then finish each sentence.

1. This poem's main idea or feeling is

   _____

   _____ .

2. Some describing words that the writer uses are

   _____

   _____ .

3. Some examples of more specific words that the writer might use are

   _____

   _____ .

Name of Reader _____

Sentence Structure: Subject-Verb-Object

The **subject** is what or whom the sentence is about. The **verb** tells what the subject does. The **object** receives the action of the verb. You can write good sentences by knowing how to put these parts of a sentence in order.

Carlos threw the ball.

subject   verb   object

Write the words in the correct order. The first sentence has been done for you.

1. bike   new   Sarah   her   rode

 Sarah rode her new bike.

2. The   dinner   dog   his   ate

_____

3. a   My   letter   wrote   dad

_____

4. a   story   told   Rob   funny

_____

5. finished   her   Beth   math   homework

_____

More Sentences with *is, are, was, were*

> You can use *is, are, was,* and *were* as **helping verbs** with other verbs that end in -*ing*.
>
> Dad **is** washing the car today.
>
> Dad **was** washing the car yesterday.

Choose words from the boxes and write sentences. Then write two sentences of your own. The first sentence has been done for you.

My grandparents	is	listening to music
Julio	are	reading a book
My mom	was	playing a game
Kim and Kelly	were	taking a walk

1. <u>My grandparents are taking a walk.</u>

2. _____

3. _____

4. _____

5. _____

6. _____

Taking Tests

Here is a question about *Our Leaders, Our Helpers:*

What are the different kinds of government in the United States? (page 7)

Ⓐ the Capitol Building

Ⓑ a local government

Ⓒ a group of people in charge

🅓 federal, state, and local governments

What is the question asking for? It is asking for the different kinds of government.

- Is the Capitol Building a kind of government? No, it is where the federal government works.

- Is a local government the answer? No, it is only one kind of government.

- Are people in charge the different kinds of government? No, the group in charge is only part of a government.

- Are federal, state, and local governments different kinds of government? Yes. They are three kinds of government. D is the correct answer.

- Look back at page 7 in *Our Leaders, Our Helpers* to confirm your answer.

Look at the questions on the next page.

Taking Tests

Look at each answer choice. Is it the right answer to the question? Why or why not?

1. **What is a democracy?** (Page 11)

   (A) country that has a president
   (B) the way a family plans its vacation
   (C) electing as leader the person with the most votes
   (D) the way a community casts ballots

2. **Reread pages 12–13. What is the main idea?** (Page 12)

   (A) Local governments take care of the community.
   (B) Fire stations and ball fields are in the community.
   (C) Your community has places like these.
   (D) City buses and playgrounds help people.

3. **What helps you understand taxes?** (Page 17)

   (A) The picture of people building a road.
   (B) The text box about different kinds of taxes.
   (C) The picture of dollar bills.
   (D) The information about tax fairness.

4. **What happens after people sign a petition to create a new law?** (Page 23)

   (A) People learn more about the issue.
   (B) The law is passed.
   (C) Someone gets an idea.
   (D) People can vote for or against the idea.

My Weekly Planner

Week of _____

Theme Vocabulary	_____
Differentiated Vocabulary	_____
Comprehension Strategy and Skill	Strategy: _____ Skill: _____
Vocabulary Strategy	_____
Spelling Skill	_____
Fluency	Selection: _____
Writing and Language Arts	Writing form: _____
Grammar	Grammar skill: _____

Newspaper Article

Read this newspaper article aloud.

Safety on Our Streets

by Cayden Fairweather

Yesterday Crestwood got a new traffic light. It is at the corner of Park Road and Elm Street. The police said there were 32 accidents here last year.

The Crestwood Community Group knocked on doors and explained the problem. They asked people to sign a petition for a traffic signal.

"Just crossing the street was dangerous," said Yolanda Garcia, one of the group's members. "Almost every week we heard people honking their horns. We're lucky no one was hurt at this corner."

Garcia spoke to the town council. She reported the accident numbers and asked for a new traffic signal.

"I was nervous about speaking in front of the town council," Garcia said. "But it was worth it!"

How well did you read? Circle your answer.

Sentence Completion

Fill in the blanks to complete the sentences.
The first item has been done for you.

1. When our class visited the fire **department,**
   we learned how to prevent a fire.

2. After taking a test, you should always **check**

   _____

3. At the store we went to the shoe **department**

   _____

4. Officer Sue of the Police **Department** visited

   our school to _____

5. When I went to the doctor last week, the

   doctor **checked** my _____

6. My favorite **department** in the store is

   _____

7. When I saw the dentist last month, he

   checked _____

8. If a lamp doesn't work, **check** to see whether

   it is _____

Word Wheels

Fill in the wheel with the names of different departments in a big store.

Fill in the wheel with the names of things you might check.

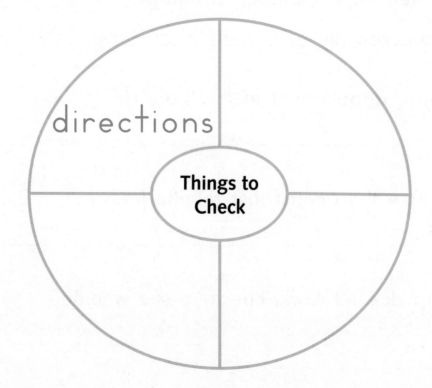

Irregular Plurals

Some nouns form their plurals in an irregular
way instead of with -s or -es.

feet	women	men	people	them
mice	geese	teeth	children	family

Write the plural of each word.

1. mouse _____

2. goose _____

3. foot _____

4. woman _____

5. tooth _____

6. man _____

7. child _____

8. person _____

Finish each sentence with a spelling word.

1. There are three children in my _____ .

2. When we visit my grandparents, we always
have dinner with _____ .

183

Monitor Comprehension

As you read, keep checking your understanding. If you don't understand something, use one or more of the fix-up strategies shown below.

Reread more slowly.	Look for clues in the pictures.
Look up words.	Read on.
Look for clues in the text.	

**Read the story. Stop to check your understanding.
Fill in the chart.**

Many people in our community thought skateboarding was unsafe. They thought the skaters could run into other people or get hit by cars. The town solved the problem by building a skateboarding park.

What did not make sense	Why did people think skateboarding was unsafe?
My fix-up strategy	I read on.
How the strategy helped	I learned that people thought skaters could hurt other people or get hit by cars.

Read the story. Stop to check your understanding. Fill in the chart.

Jake and his dad wheeled their bikes out of the garage. Jake was going on his first ride on the town's bike path. They rode to the bike path. Then Jake's dad told Jake about the "rules of the road."

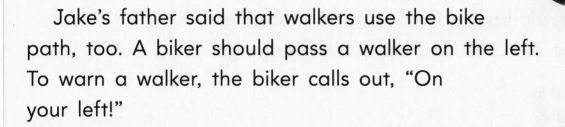

Jake's father said that walkers use the bike path, too. A biker should pass a walker on the left. To warn a walker, the biker calls out, "On your left!"

What did not make sense	
My fix-up strategy	
How the strategy helped	

Multiple Meaning Words

Multiple-meaning words

- have more than one meaning
- are spelled and pronounced the same way
- may be different parts of speech

Clues in the text can help you figure out the correct meaning of these words.

The word *train* has more than one meaning. Look at the pictures and read the meanings.

railroad cars

to teach skills

Read the sentence. Fill in the chart to figure out the correct meaning of *train*.

I trained my new puppy to fetch a stick.

Clues	new puppy, fetch a stick
What I Know	You can train a pet to learn new skills.
Meaning	In this sentence, *train* means to teach skills.

Circle the correct meaning of the underlined
word in each sentence.

1.

The player began to <u>tire</u> after the first
quarter of the game.

the rubber part of a wheel   to become worn out

2.

I drink a <u>glass</u> of milk every day for
breakfast.

the clear part of a window   a container for a drink

3.

My dog starts to <u>bark</u> when
someone rings our doorbell.

to make a short, loud cry   the outer layer of a
tree trunk

4.

We had a great view from the <u>top</u> of
the mountain.

a toy that spins   the highest point

Before and After Reading

Look at the cover of *Officer Buckle and Gloria*.

Read these statements. Write a check mark in the box beside the statement if you think that it is true. Write an X if you think it is false. Do this before and after you read to see how much you were able to guess from the cover.

Before	Officer Buckle and Gloria	After
	This story will be about something that happens in real life.	
	Officer Buckle is a police officer.	
	Gloria is a cat.	
	The story will be very sad.	
	Officer Buckle will do something to help his community.	

Plot: Problem and Solution

A **plot** is the series of events that take place in the story. Often the plot is about a problem and how it is solved.

Read the story. Then fill in the solution box.

Josh had a problem. He had four sisters and no brothers. There were no boys in his neighborhood.

Josh played with a new action figure. It was fun for a while, but he wished he had a friend to play with. Then Josh heard a truck. From the window he saw a moving truck. It pulled into the driveway next door. Josh watched the movers unpack the truck. Josh thought, "The family will probably have all girls!"

After dinner, Josh went out to the porch. The moving van was gone. Then a car pulled into the driveway. A mother and a father got out. Josh held his breath. Finally, the back doors of the car opened. Josh couldn't believe his eyes. Three boys piled out of the car. They saw Josh and waved. Josh waved back with a big grin on his face.

Problem	Solution
Josh had no one to play with.	

Read and Respond

Think about what you read in *Officer Buckle and Gloria*. Then answer the questions.

1. What was your favorite part of the story?

_____

_____

2. Do you think that Gloria was a good friend to Officer Buckle?

_____

_____

3. Write a message to send to Officer Buckle.

_____

_____

_____

_____

_____

Recall and Retell

To **recall** and **retell** a story can help you understand and remember it.

- When you recall, you think about what you have read.

- When you retell, you tell the story in your own words.

Recall what happened when Gloria helped Officer Buckle present safety tips. Write what you remember.

_____

_____

_____

_____

_____

**Retell this part of the story to a partner.
Use your own words.**

Unit 7, Project 2

Inquiry Planner

My Plan for Next Week

1. The Inquiry question is:

   _____

   _____

2. What information will I collect?

   _____

3. How will I collect information?

   ☐ Books   ☐ Talking to people

   ☐ Other _____

4. Where will I collect information?

   ☐ My classroom   ☐ My school library
   ☐ At home   ☐ In my community

   ☐ Other _____

5. When will I collect information?

   ☐ During Self-Selected Reading time
   ☐ During Independent Practice time
   ☐ After school

Focus Question
How does a local government help make a good community?

How was local government helpful in this story? Choose one of the characters from your book to give your answer. Draw the character and fill in the speech bubble.

Character's Name: _____

What role does local government play in my community? Write your answer.

_____
_____
_____

Focus Question
What is the relationship between my local government and me?

Look at these pictures. How are these people getting involved with local government? Write what each picture shows. Tell how the people in the picture are helping the community.

_____

_____

_____

_____

_____

_____

_____

_____

_____

_____

_____

_____

My Weekly Planner

Week of _____

Theme Vocabulary	_____
Differentiated Vocabulary	_____
Comprehension Strategy and Skill	Strategy: _____ Skill: _____
Vocabulary Strategy	_____
Spelling Skill	_____
Fluency	Selection: _____
Writing and Language Arts	Writing form: _____
Grammar	Grammar skill: _____

Short Story

Read this short story aloud.

The Library Book
by Jess Mayer

Someone had dropped a library book on the sidewalk. I looked around to see who might have left it behind, but I didn't see anyone.

I walked over to the library. The librarian was glad I returned the book. She said, "Do you know what happens when people lose library books? The library loses money, and without money, the library cannot buy new books." She sounded serious.

She said, "I'll check the book in our computer system," she explained. After a minute or two, she told me that the book was past due.

I started to explain that it wasn't my book.

She laughed and said, "I can see on the computer that you did not check it out. Your brother did. When you see him, please tell him what I said."

How well did you read? Circle your answer.

Idea Completion

government	agree	elect	checked
department	taxes	issue	

Choose a word to complete each sentence. The first item has been done for you.

1. An early American <u>government</u> agreed on a plan.

2. Every four years, voters _____ a new President.

3. There are no _____ on food in our state.

4. We all _____ that it is important to stay healthy.

5. Keeping our water clean is an important health _____ .

6. The government has a _____ to repair roads.

7. This morning, I _____ to make sure my homework was in my backpack.

Connect Words

issue	government	agree	vote
taxes	recycling	elect	safety

Use two words from the box in each sentence that you write below. The first item has been done for you.

1. <u>Most people agree that we need taxes.</u>

2. _____

_____

3. _____

_____

4. _____

_____

Prefixes

The prefixes *un-* and *re-* change the meaning of words.

unlock	unhappy	retell	remake	upon
unzip	unsafe	repaint	reread	once

Rewrite the underlined word in each sentence by adding *un-*.

1. <u>Lock</u> the door and let me in.   <u>unlock</u>

2. Being sick makes me <u>happy</u>.   _____

3. Crossing a city street can be <u>safe</u>.   _____

Rewrite the underlined word in each sentence by adding *re-*.

4. I liked the story so much that I wanted to <u>read</u> it.   _____

5. My airplane model fell apart, so I had to <u>make</u> it.   _____

6. I asked my grandpa to <u>tell</u> my favorite story.   _____

Finish the sentence with two other spelling words.

7. Fairy tales often begin with a sentence containing these two spelling words: _____ a time.

Ask and Answer Questions

Ask questions to check your understanding. Then **answer** your questions.

Follow these steps:

1. **Ask** a question about what you have read.
2. **Look** for clues in the text to answer your question.
3. **Use** what you already know.
4. **Answer** your question.

Read the story, then fill in the chart.

The town created a new pedestrian mall downtown. Cars can't drive down the street anymore. There are planters with flowers in the middle of the street and places to sit. People can walk back and forth between stores on both sides of the street.

Ask a question	What is a pedestrian mall?
Clues in the text	planters and places to sit in the street, no cars, people walking
What I know	shopping malls are places where people walk from store to store
Answer	A pedestrian mall must be a place where people can walk from store to store. The town created it by removing cars from a street with stores.

Read the story, then fill in the chart.

Local governments need to make rules about pets. Most people have cats and dogs as pets. However, some people have pets that become a problem for a community.

In Florida, a man kept alligators as pets. Neighbors worried about what would happen if the alligators escaped from their pens. The town council decided that alligators could not be kept as pets. Now the alligators live in a nature preserve.

Ask a question	
Clues in the text	
What I know	
Answer	

Use Multiple Strategies

An **idiom** is a phrase whose meaning is different from that of the individual words.

Read the idiom. Then write the meaning of the idiom.

Tim and I <u>put our heads together</u> and got our project done.

What does the idiom mean?

<u>worked together</u>

With **multiple-meaning words,** the meaning depends on how the word is used. The noun *figure* can mean a number, such as 2, or a geometric shape, such as a circle.

Read the sentence. Then write the meaning of the word *figure*.

A closed figure that has four straight sides is a rectangle.

What does the word *figure* mean?

<u>geometric shape</u>

Read the idiom. Then write the meaning of the idiom.

1. The team felt <u>on top of the world</u> when they won the game.

   What is the meaning of the idiom?

_____

2. James was not in school today because he was <u>under the weather</u>.

   What is the meaning of the idiom?

_____

_____

Read the sentence. Then circle the meaning of the word *sign*.

I need to sign my letter to Grandma.

to use sign language   to write your name

Before and After Reading

Read each question. Before you read the story, write *yes, no,* or *maybe* in the left column. After you read the story, write the answer in the right column.

Before	A Helping Hand	After
	1. Are volunteers paid to do their jobs?	
	2. Do volunteers organize parades?	
	3. Can a young person be a volunteer?	

Before	Getting Involved	After
	1. Do young people have the right to vote?	
	2. Can a person your age write to the town council?	
	3. Is a petition a good way to make changes?	

Safe and Well

Before		After
_____	**1.** Does local government inspect a school cafeteria?	_____
_____	**2.** Are city parks run by businesses?	_____
_____	**3.** Do communities keep houses and factories in separate places?	_____

Working for You

Before		After
_____	**1.** Does the government keep a record of when you were born?	_____
_____	**2.** Can you borrow books from a library for free?	_____
_____	**3.** Would the government take care of a homeless animal?	_____

Sequence Events

Sequence is the order in which events take place. A sequence of events has a beginning, a middle, and an end.

Read the story. Fill in the chart with the events in the correct sequence.

How can you make changes in your community? First, learn more about an issue. Next, ask people to sign a petition about the issue. Then ask the government to put the issue on the ballot. Finally, ask voters to support your issue when they vote.

First
Learn more about an issue.

↓

Next

↓

Then

↓

Finally

Prepare to Present

Class Inquiry Question: _____

_____

Circle one for each.

1. What does your research show?

2. How will you share your findings?

steps in a process

relationships

cause and effect

a story

how something works

| Diagram |
| Book of Illustrations |

| Diagram | Skit |
| Puppet Show | Mural |

Chart or Diagram
Skit
Puppet Show
Book of Illustrations

| Picture Book | Skit |
| Puppet Show | |

| Diagram | Mural |
| Picture Book | |

Focus Question

What is the relationship between my local government and me?

How am I connected to my local government? Write your ideas in the wheel. Write the name of your community in the center of the wheel.

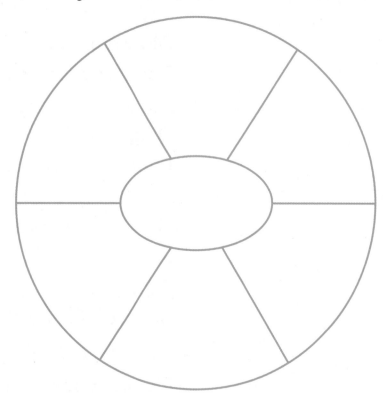

What role does the government play in my community? Write your answer.

_____

_____

_____

Study the Model

Descriptive Paragraph

Read the Writing Model along with your teacher. Look for a topic sentence, supporting sentences, and a closing sentence in the paragraph.

My Tree

by Nori Adkins

We have a huge, old tree in our backyard. In the spring and summer, it is covered in bushy clumps of sweet-smelling green leaves. I like to lean against its rough, brown trunk and sit in the cool shade. In the fall, the leaves turn a lovely tone of yellow. They glitter like gold in the sunlight and rustle in the wind. In winter, the tree is bare. I can see the big branches twist high up into the blue sky. I love my tree because it is beautiful all year round.

Study the Model

Descriptive Paragraph

Read the Writing Model along with your teacher. Look for a topic sentence, supporting sentences, and a closing sentence in the paragraph.

The Fourth of July Fireworks
by Brian Mulhaney

On the Fourth of July, our town puts on a colorful and exciting fireworks show. The show starts when the sky gets dark. A shell shoots up fast like a rocket and bursts into a bright, glowing light. Shiny sparkles fall like rain and disappear. Then—kaboom, kaboom—the sound is like a cannon in my ears. The strong smoky smell after the boom makes me pinch my nose, but I don't mind it too much. The show ends with a finale of one hundred fireworks! Our town puts on the best show.

Evaluation Rubric

Descriptive Paragraph

Writing Trait	Goals	Yes	Needs work!	Now it's OK.
Organization	My paragraph has a topic sentence, supporting sentences, and a closing sentence.			
Ideas	My paragraph gives a detailed picture of a person, place, or thing. I include enough details.			
Voice	My writing shows that I care. The voice is right for my audience.			
Word Choice	I include similes. I use sensory words.			
Sentence Fluency	I vary my sentences.			
Conventions	I capitalize proper nouns. I use a comma and a conjunction in compound sentences.			

Peer Review

Descriptive Paragraph

Read your partner's paper. Then finish each sentence.

1. The writer is describing

_____

_____

_____ .

2. Some examples of details in the paragraph are

_____

_____

_____ .

3. The writer might use strong sensory words like

_____

_____

_____ .

Name of Reader _____

Compound Sentences

You can combine two sentences to make a **compound sentence** by using the word *and, or,* or *but.*

| The dog barked. | **+** | The cat meowed. |

Compound sentence: The dog barked, **and** the cat meowed.

comma Add *and*

Combine the sentences to make a compound sentence. Add a comma before *and, but,* or *or.*

1. Jason is my brother. Maria is my sister.

Jason is my brother, and Maria is my sister.

2. My mother is tall. My father is taller.

_____

_____

3. I will sweep the floor. My sister will do that chore.

_____

_____

Punctuating Dialogue

Use **quotation marks** before and after a person's words. Place a comma or a period before the end quotation marks.

Jamie and Clare are coming with us   said Angie.

Hubert said   I need help

Read each sentence. Write _C_ if the punctuation is correct. Write _I_ if it is incorrect. The first item has been done for you.

1. "Our class pet is missing," Claire shouted. ___C___

2. "I'll help look for it," said Tim. _____

3. "I know where it might be" Jamie said. _____

4. Laura said, "I think it's in the bookcase." _____

5. Tim yelled, I found our hamster." _____

6. "He looks scared" Jamie said. _____

Write the last sentence for the story, using quotation marks.

7. _____

_____

Taking Tests

Here is a question about *Officer Buckle and Gloria.*

Why did the children love Officer Buckle's speech when Gloria came along? Draw a conclusion.

How can you answer this question? First, look at the words in the question. The question asks you to draw a conclusion. To draw a conclusion, you think about all of the information in the story and reach a new decision or understanding.

Information from Text	Gloria stands on her head, and the children's eyes pop. Gloria jumps into the air, and the children roar.
What I Know	It's easier to learn something when it's fun.

Conclusion: Gloria made Officer Buckle's safety tips interesting and funny by acting them out. The children loved Gloria's performance.

Taking Tests

Here is another question about *Officer Buckle and Gloria.*

Why did Officer Buckle say, "Always stick with your buddy" at the end of the story? Draw a conclusion.

Information from Text	
What I Know	

Write your conclusion. Provide reasons for your answer.

_____

_____

_____

_____

My Weekly Planner

Week of _____

Theme Vocabulary	_____
Differentiated Vocabulary	_____
Comprehension Strategy and Skill	Strategy: _____ Skill: _____
Vocabulary Strategy	_____
Spelling Skill	_____
Fluency	Selection: _____
Writing and Language Arts	Writing form: _____
Grammar	Grammar skill: _____

E-Mail

Read this e-mail aloud.

Fit as a Fiddle
by Merce Goodman

Guess what! I won a prize in our school fitness challenge. Three months ago everyone in the whole school took a fitness test. We ran the hundred-yard dash, and we were timed. For me, it wasn't really a dash. Then we did push-ups and sit-ups while our teachers counted them. I wasn't too happy with my numbers.

My friends and I worked hard to improve. During recess we helped each other time our runs and cheered each other on. We did sit-ups and push-ups too. It's easier to work out if you're doing it with friends.

Yesterday we took the test again, and all of us had improved! There were prizes for the fastest runners and the people who did the most push-ups and sit-ups. The biggest prize, though, went to the person who improved the most—me!

How well did you read? Circle your answer.

Answer Questions

Write *yes* or *no* to answer each question.

1. Can scientists **control** the weather? _____

2. Does a steering wheel **control** a car? _____

3. Is being brave a **weakness**? _____

4. Is a powerful person **weak**? _____

5. Do you have any **weaknesses**? _____

6. Do traffic guards **control** traffic? _____

Write a sentence using the word *weakness* or *control*.

_____

_____

Idea Completion

Complete each sentence.

1. The policeman **controlled** the traffic by

   telling the cars to stop _____

   _____ .

2. Jon's **weakness** was

   _____

   _____ .

3. The person who **controls** your school is

   _____

   _____ .

4. If you had a **weakness** in playing sports, you could

   _____

   _____ .

Suffixes *-ly*, *-ful*

The suffixes *-ly* and *-ful* change one part of speech to another.

helpful	painful	wildly	badly	happily
spoonful	playful	softly	wisely	beautiful

Use a spelling word to complete each sentence.

1. The _playful_ kitten ran all around the house.

2. The wind blew so _____ that it broke branches off trees.

3. My coach gave us _____ advice.

4. When the baby sleeps, we try to speak _____.

5. On my birthday, I _____ opened my presents.

6. A broken leg is very _____.

7. We planted _____ flowers in our garden.

8. Our team played _____, so we lost the game.

9. The nurse gave the child a _____ of medicine.

10. My father _____ said to watch for traffic.

Make Predictions

When you **make predictions**, you

- use information from the text and what you already know

- guess what will happen next

Read the story and make a prediction.

Jenny and Jessie were sisters. Both were good runners. They planned to run in a race. Jenny began training a month before the race. Jessie had always been faster. She didn't think she needed to train. The day of the race came. When the runners took off, Jessie pulled ahead of Jenny.

From the Text	Jenny trained. Jessie was faster.
What I Know	Training helps runners.
Prediction	Jessie will win.

Read the end of the story.

Jenny caught up with Jessie and won the race!

Was your prediction correct?

Read the story and make a prediction.

Rob wanted to play basketball. No one asked him to play because he was short for his age.

Every night, Rob played basketball with his dad. Rob dreamed of being taller.

One day Rob was watching a basketball game. He wanted to try the shot he had practiced. Rob walked onto the court. "Hey, do you need another player?" he asked.

One boy said, "Sure. You can be on our team."

Important Story Clues	
What I Know	
Prediction	

Read the end of the story.

Finally Rob got the ball. He made the jump shot. SWOOSH! It was Rob's first basket, but not his last.

Was your prediction right?

Metaphors

A **metaphor**

- compares two different things

- creates a picture in the reader's mind

Metaphor: My brother is an encyclopedia.

Meaning of metaphor:

My brother is smart and knows many things.

Read the metaphor. Write the meaning.

Metaphor: The football player is a two-ton truck.

Meaning of metaphor:

The football player is tall, wide, and powerful.

Read the metaphor. Then write its meaning.

1.

   Metaphor: The tree was a leafy umbrella on a hot day.

   Meaning of metaphor:

   _____

   _____

2.

   Metaphor: Her eyes were sparkling jewels.

   Meaning of metaphor:

   _____

   _____

3.

   Metaphor: My baby brother is a bundle of joy.

   Meaning of metaphor:

   _____

   _____

Details and Facts

Details and facts:

- give information about important ideas

- describe the characters or setting in a story

- give examples or facts about a topic

- help readers understand what they are reading

Read. Look for details and facts about Winter Olympic athletes. Write them in the web.

The Winter Olympic Games are held every four years. Athletes from all around the world gather to compete. Skiers race down mountains and try amazing jumps. Figure skaters spin and jump on the ice. Bobsledders race at high speeds down twisting tracks. Snowboarders do tricks on special ramps.

Skiers race.

How Winter Olympic Athletes Compete

Unit 8, Project 1

Inquiry Planner

My Plan for Next Week

1. The Inquiry question is:

_____

_____

2. What information will I collect?

_____

3. How will I collect information?

☐ Books   ☐ Talking to people

☐ Other _____

4. Where will I collect information?

☐ My classroom   ☐ My school library
☐ At home   ☐ In my community

☐ Other _____

5. When will I collect information?

☐ During Self-Selected Reading time
☐ During Independent Practice time
☐ After school

Prepare to Present

Class Inquiry Question:

_____

Circle one for each.

1. What does your research show?

2. How will you share your findings?

steps in a process

relationships

cause and effect

a story

how something works

| Diagram |
| Book of Illustrations |

| Diagram | Skit |
| Puppet Show | Mural |

| Chart or Diagram |
| Skit |
| Puppet Show |
| Book of Illustrations |

| Picture Book |
| Skit |
| Puppet Show |

| Diagram |
| Mural |
| Picture Book |

Focus Question
What is a physical feat?

Write a definition of a physical feat.

_____

_____

What sports or activities have you read about
this week?

_____

_____

Explain why one sport or activity you read
about is a physical feat.

_____

_____

What does it take to overcome a challenge?
Write your answer.

_____

_____

Focus Question

What does physical strength represent in literature?

Look at these pictures. How are these people performing physical feats?

_____

_____

_____

_____

_____

_____

My Weekly Planner

Week of _____

Theme Vocabulary	_____
Differentiated Vocabulary	_____
Comprehension Strategy and Skill	Strategy: _____ Skill: _____
Vocabulary Strategy	_____
Spelling Skill	_____
Fluency	Selection: _____
Writing and Language Arts	Writing form: _____
Grammar	Grammar skill: _____

Poem

Read this poem aloud.

Real-Life Heroes
by Cary Tompkins

Heroes in movies can fly through the sky
and pick up a car without blinking an eye.

Real heroes are strong—in ways they can show,
but also in ways that some never know.

A true hero might say, "That is not right."
She'd point out unfairness and bring it to light.

A hero in real life might put her foot down
To stand up for friends, herself, and her town.

A hero in real life might walk with someone
who's scared of a bully. That's really no fun.

Heroes in legends fight monsters and win.
Heroes in real life fight struggles within.

Heroes are strong—in ways they can show
but also in ways that some never know.

How well did you read? Circle your answer.

Draw It

Draw something about the words *compete* and *defeated*. Use both words in a sentence about your picture.

Compete and Defeated

_____

_____

Draw a picture that shows one of your goals. Write a sentence about your goal.

My Goal

_____

Brainstorming

Words that share the same root have similar meanings.

compete (verb)—to try to win

competition (noun)—a contest that people try to win

competitor (noun)—someone who tries to win

Complete each sentence with a word from the box.

1. Our soccer team will <u>compete</u> in a tournament next Saturday.

2. We will play against other _____ who are great players.

3. We think that we will win the _____.

Write three sentences using words from the box.

1. _____

2. _____

3. _____

Compound Words

A **compound word** is made up of two smaller words.

cannot	playground	myself	outside	everybody
baseball	sunshine	classroom	popcorn	everything

Add a word to each small word to make a spelling word.

1. _every_ body

2. base _____

3. _____ room

4. _____ ground

5. out _____

6. sun _____

7. every _____

8. can _____

9. my _____

10. pop _____

Write a sentence that uses two spelling words.

_____

_____

_____

Make Inferences

When you read, you add what you already know to what the author tells you. This is called **making an inference**.

| What I Read | **+** | What I Know | **=** | Inference: A New Thought or Idea |

Read the story.

Coyote was hungry. He was out prowling during the night. Suddenly he saw two eyes shining in the dark. He got ready to pounce. Then he saw the animal raise its black and white tail.

Coyote stopped, but not soon enough. He ran to the river to wash off the terrible smell!

Make an inference.

What animal fooled Coyote?

a skunk

Read the story.

Monkey was swinging through the treetops. He reached out to pluck a banana, but he lost his balance! He fell to the ground.

Monkey picked himself up. Then he saw Tiger staring at him. Monkey shrieked and started to run. He leaped and hopped through the forest. Tiger was right behind.

Monkey saw a tall tree. He jumped high and landed on a branch. Tiger tried to climb the tree, but his claws couldn't reach Monkey.

Tiger grinned and said, "I'll wait for you, Monkey."

Monkey knew that he couldn't stay in the tree forever. He needed a plan. He shook one of the branches. Suddenly, something big, round, and hard fell out of the tree and hit Tiger on the head. With a growl, Tiger ran away. Monkey sat on the branch and howled with laughter.

Make inferences.

What fell out of the tree and hit Tiger?

_____

_____

_____

Synonyms

Synonyms are words that have the same or nearly the same meaning.

| large huge | silly funny | find discover |

Knowing synonyms can help you figure out unfamiliar words.

> The soldier showed great **courage**. Everyone admired his (bravery).

Courage and *bravery* are synonyms. The word *bravery* helps you understand that *courage* means "the ability to do things without fear."

Read the sentence. Circle the word or words that help you understand the word in dark type.

The athlete's **ambition** was to be the best in the world. He had set himself a (high goal).

**Read the sentences. Circle the word or words
that help you understand the word in dark
type. Then write another sentence that contains
the word in dark type.**

1. They drove down the road along the **coast**. They
saw the beach and ocean through the window.

   A *coast* is _____

   _____

2. The boy was **intelligent**. Everyone thought that
he was a smart child.

   An *intelligent* person is _____

   _____

3. The children were making a terrible **racket** upstairs.

   "Stop making so much noise!" called Mom.

   A *racket* is _____

   _____

4. The town **expanded** every year. New buildings
appeared as the town grew bigger.

   To *expand* means _____

   _____

Compare and Contrast

When you **compare** two things, you think about how they are alike.

When you **contrast** two things, you think about how they are different.

You can use a diagram to compare and contrast two things.

Compare and contrast a runner and a swimmer.

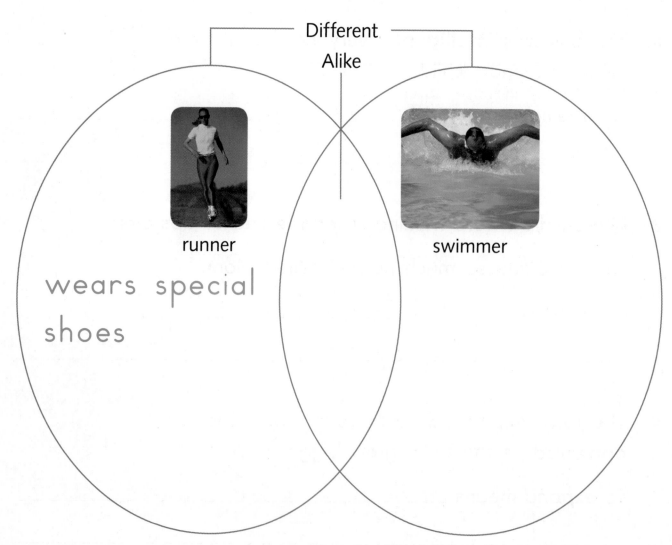

Different

Alike

runner

swimmer

wears special shoes

Think Back
Selection 2

Focus Question
What does physical strength represent in literature?

How do the characters in the story show physical strength? Write your answer.

Name of Character: _____

_____

_____

Name of Character: _____

_____

_____

What does it take to overcome a challenge?
Write your answer.

_____

_____

_____

241

Focus Question

Why do brains beat physical strength in literature?

Look at these pictures. How do you think they show strength or smarts?

Write your answer.

_____

_____

_____

_____

_____

_____

Study the Model

Friendly Letter

Read the Writing Model along with your teacher. Look for the heading, greeting, and body of the letter.

4000 Desert Lane
Phoenix, AZ 85042

May 24, 2010

Dear Cindi,

Our class went to the zoo yesterday. We saw a lot of animals eating, playing, and sleeping.

I really liked the giraffes! We watched them use their long, beautiful necks to reach the leaves in tall trees.

I had no problem getting around in my wheelchair. The zoo has smooth ramps, and most of the buildings have automatic doors.

How's your new school? I hope you can visit soon!

Your friend,

Keely

Study the Model

Thank-You Note and Invitation

Model 1

> Dear Aunt Stephanie,
>
> Thank you for the lab kit! I'll have lots of fun making lava, invisible ink, and lots of other cool stuff. Mom says it will be exercise for my brain. It's a great gift!
>
> Love,

Model 2

> Mia's 8! Come celebrate!
>
> What: My Birthday Party with Pizza, Cake, Balloons, Games, and More
>
> When: Saturday, June 5, 2010, 1:00 p.m.
>
> Where: Mario's Pizzeria, 2323 Main St., Springfield
>
> Please let us know if you can come!

Evaluation Rubric

Messages

Writing Trait	Goals	Yes	Needs work!	Now it's OK.
Organization	I include all the parts of my message.			
Ideas	I share ideas and events with my friend. I thank someone for a gift, favor, or service.			
Voice	The tone of my message is friendly.			
Word Choice	I use interesting, descriptive words.			
Sentence Fluency	I vary the beginnings of my sentences. I combine sentences to make them less choppy.			
Conventions	All of the words are spelled correctly. I use correct punctuation. I indent the paragraphs.			

Peer Review

Messages

Read your partner's paper. Then finish each sentence.

1. The topic of this message is

_____

_____

_____.

2. The purpose of this message is

_____

_____

_____.

3. The writer uses interesting, descriptive words like

_____

_____

_____.

Name of Reader _____

Capitalization

Proper nouns begin with capital letters. The names for days of the week, months, and holidays are all proper nouns that need to be capitalized. Book titles also begin with capital letters.

Month	January
Holiday	Thanksgiving
Day	Friday
Book title	*Charlotte's Web*

Rewrite each sentence. Replace the underlined phrase with a proper noun from the box.

July	*Mother Goose Tales*
Halloween	

1. We wear costumes on this holiday.

_____

2. I think that month is the hottest month.

_____

3. Last night we read the book.

_____

Abbreviations and Titles

Abbreviations are short forms of a word.

Green **Rd.** (Road)   Main **St.** (Street)   First **Ave.** (Avenue)

A **title** is a word used in front of a person's name.

Mr. Brown   **Mrs.** Garcia   **Ms.** Jones   **Dr.** Chen

Abbreviations and titles begin with a capital letter and end with a period.

Write the abbreviation for each word in parentheses.

1. I have an appointment with (Doctor) Harris. _____

2. My new school is located at 240 Second (Avenue) in New York City. _____

Write three sentences about yourself, using abbreviations.

1. _____

2. _____

3. _____

Taking Tests

Here is a question about *Strength and Smarts:*

What conclusion you can draw about King Arthur? (pages 14–15)

Ⓐ He liked fighting giants.
Ⓑ He was afraid of battles.
Ⓒ He was American.
Ⓓ He was brave and strong.

What does the question ask for? A conclusion about King Arthur.

- Did King Arthur like fighting giants? No, he didn't. He fought a terrifying giant, but we don't know whether he liked it.

- Was King Arthur afraid of battles? No, he wasn't. He fought a long battle.

- Was King Arthur American? No, he wasn't. He was British.

- Was King Arthur brave and strong? Yes, he was. D is the correct answer.

Look at the questions on the next page.

Taking Tests

Look at each answer choice. Is it the right answer to the question? Why or why not?

1. **What does adrenaline do?** (page 11)

   Ⓐ It makes people's muscles bigger.
   Ⓑ It helps athletes run more slowly.
   Ⓒ It makes people's hearts beat faster.
   Ⓓ It causes runners to become tired.

2. **What is a marathon?** (page 12)

   Ⓐ a Greek runner
   Ⓑ a race for disabled athletes
   Ⓒ a race of 26.2 miles
   Ⓓ a bike race

3. **What was the author's purpose in writing about Mia Hamm?** (pages 22–23)

   Ⓐ to entertain
   Ⓑ to inform
   Ⓒ to persuade
   Ⓓ to make up a story

4. **What inference can you make about April Holmes?** (pages 26–27)

   Ⓐ She felt sorry for herself.
   Ⓑ She used mind power to overcome her disability.
   Ⓒ She wanted to be famous.
   Ⓓ She was nervous about running again.

My Weekly Planner

Week of _____

Theme Vocabulary	_____
Differentiated Vocabulary	_____
Comprehension Strategy and Skill	Strategy: _____ Skill: _____
Vocabulary Strategy	_____
Spelling Skill	_____
Fluency	Selection: _____
Writing and Language Arts	Writing form: _____
Grammar	Grammar skill: _____

Joke

Read this joke aloud.

Prove It
by Crosby Sanford

A group of kids went to the park after school. One of them bragged, "I'm the strongest one here." Pointing to a smaller kid, he said, "I'm *much* stronger than you!"

The smaller kid smiled and replied, "If you're really that strong, you'll be able to prove it."

"That's right," said the big kid.

"I will carry something very heavy over to that big tree," said the smaller kid. "But there is no way you will be able to carry it back."

"Are you joking?" the big kid replied. "I can carry anything twice as far as you can!"

"We'll see," said the smaller kid. Then he picked up the big kid and carried him toward the tree.

How well did you read? Circle your answer.

Sentences

Write another word to go with the vocabulary word. Then write a sentence using both words. The first item has been done for you.

1. Word: **grabbed**   Word: sandwich

   Sentence: I grabbed a sandwich as I went out the door.

2. Word: **struggled**   Word: _____

   Sentence: _____

   _____

3. Word: **struggled**   Word: _____

   Sentence: _____

   _____

4. Word: **grabbed**   Word: _____

   Sentence: _____

   _____

Answer Questions

Fill in the word skeletons by answering the questions. The first space has been filled in for you.

an apple

What food would you **grab** to eat?

grab

What do you **grab** before you leave for school?

Who would you **grab** onto if you were afraid?

What things do you sometimes **struggle** to do?

struggle

How does it feel when you **struggle**?

When do people have to **struggle** against nature?

Commonly Misspelled Words

Some words sound the same but have different spellings and meanings.

weak	road	tale	be	there
week	rode	tail	bee	their

**Write the spelling word that goes with each clue.
The first one has been done for you.**

1. You can drive a car on one.   road

2. An insect that makes honey   _____

3. A dog wags this   _____

4. The past tense of *ride*   _____

5. The opposite of *here*   _____

6. This has seven days   _____

7. A story   _____

8. A helping verb   _____

Finish the sentences with spelling words.

1. The doctor said that I would be less
   _____ in a _____.

2. My brothers parked _____ bikes
   over _____.

Make Connections

When you read, you **make connections** between the text and:

| something you have read | your own experiences | what you know about the world |

Look at the connections a reader made to *My Lucky Day*.

In the Text	**This Reminds Me of**	**Connection**
One character is a piglet.	the story called *The Three Little Pigs*.	☑ Text ○ Self ○ World

In the Text	**This Reminds Me of**	**Connection**
Fox gave the piglet a bath.	My mom gives my baby brother a bath every night.	○ Text ☑ Self ○ World

256

Read the story.

Luke was a talented gymnast. His coach asked him to try out for the Junior Olympics. Luke practiced his routine over and over.

On the day before the competition, Luke practiced one last time. At the end, he fell. His ankle started to swell. Luke's eyes filled with tears. He knew that his dream was over.

His coach came up and patted him on the back. "You've had bad luck," he said to Luke. "But there will always be another competition."

Make connections to the text. Write in the boxes.

In the Text	This Reminds Me of	Connection
		○ Text ○ Self ○ World

In the Text	This Reminds Me of	Connection
		○ Text ○ Self ○ World

Picture Clues

When you see an unknown word, look at the pictures nearby. They may give you **picture clues** that can help you understand the word.

Circle the picture clues. Then write the meaning of the word in dark type.

International meetings take place here.

International means <u>from countries all over the world.</u>

Circle the picture clues. Then write the meaning of each word in dark type.

1.
A gymnast must have good **balance**.

Balance means

_____

_____

2.
Knights wore **armor** to protect them during battles.

Armor is

_____

_____

3.
The school **choir** sang songs for the students.

A *choir* is

_____

_____

Before and After Reading

Read these statements. Before you read the story, write *Y* for *yes* or *N* for *no* in the blank space before each statement. After you read, do the same thing in the space after each statement. See how many statements you predicted correctly.

Before	My Lucky Day	After
	The story is a fantasy.	
	The fox and the pig are friends.	
	The fox is smarter than the pig.	
	The fox will eat the pig.	
	The story has a happy ending.	

Character

Read the story. Answer the questions about the characters.

Once, a little mouse was running through the forest. He ran right onto a sleeping lion's back. The lion woke up with a roar.

"You ruined my nap!" the lion growled. "I'll have to eat you." The lion grabbed the little mouse.

"Please don't eat me," the mouse squeaked. "Some day I will return your kindness."

The lion laughed so hard that the little mouse fell out of his paw.

A week later, the lion walked into a hunter's trap!

The little mouse heard the lion roaring. He ran onto the lion's back and began to chew the ropes. "Thank you, little mouse," the lion said. "I've learned that little friends can be great friends!"

1. What does the lion say first to the mouse? What kind of character is the lion?

_____

2. What does the mouse say to the lion? What kind of character is the mouse?

_____

Read and Respond

**Think about what you read in *My Lucky Day*.
Then answer the questions.**

1. What was your favorite picture in the book?

_____

_____

_____

2. Did you think that the fox was going to eat the pig?

_____

_____

_____

3. Would you change the ending of the story?

_____

_____

_____

Author's Purpose

An **author** has a **purpose**, or reason, for writing.

Author's Purpose	
to inform	give readers information
to entertain	tell a funny or interesting story
to persuade	try to get readers to do something

Read the story.

Pig decided to run a marathon. He put running shoes on and practiced standing up. He fell down ten times! Finally he took off running. He didn't get far.

"I think I have to lose some weight," Pig squealed.

Pig went home. The running had made him hungry. He ate four apples and a bowl of ice cream.

Pig kicked off his shoes and lay down on the sofa. He turned on the TV. A marathon was on! Pig fell asleep and dreamed that he had won the marathon!

Check the author's purpose.

☐ to inform   ☐ to entertain   ☐ to persuade

How do you know?

_____

Unit 8, Project 2

Inquiry Planner

My Plan for Next Week

1. The Inquiry question is:

_____

_____

2. What information will I collect?

_____

3. How will I collect information?

☐ Books   ☐ Talking to people

☐ Other _____

4. Where will I collect information?

☐ My classroom   ☐ My school library
☐ At home   ☐ In my community

☐ Other _____

5. When will I collect information?

☐ During Self-Selected Reading time
☐ During Independent Practice time
☐ After school

Think Back
Selection 3

Focus Question

Why do brains beat physical strength in literature?

How did the character in your story use his or her smarts to compete? Fill in the chart.

Character's Name	How the Character Used His or Her Smarts

What does it take to overcome a challenge?

Write your answer.

_____

_____

_____

_____

_____

Focus Question
How do brains and muscles work together to help people succeed?

How might these people use strength and smarts to overcome a challenge? Write your answers.

My Weekly Planner

Week of _____

Theme Vocabulary	_____
Differentiated Vocabulary	_____
Comprehension Strategy and Skill	Strategy: _____ Skill: _____
Vocabulary Strategy	_____
Spelling Skill	_____
Fluency	Selection: _____
Writing and Language Arts	Writing form: _____
Grammar	Grammar skill: _____

Speech

Read this speech aloud.

A Person I Admire
by Cory Morgenstern

Today, I would like to honor a heroic woman. Harriet Tubman was born into slavery in Maryland around 1820. Today slavery is against the law. Slavery takes away people's freedom. Harriet Tubman knew that everyone has a right to be free.

So, in 1849 Harriet ran away from the plantation where she was enslaved. She traveled at night, using the North Star as a guide. She walked more than 100 miles to Philadelphia. This heroic woman didn't stop there. Once she was free, she found a way to free others.

Harriet returned to Maryland to save members of her family. Then she helped others. On her own Harriet helped about 300 slaves reach freedom. This was a very dangerous thing to do. That is why I'd like to honor Harriet Tubman as a truly heroic woman.

How well did you read? Circle your answer.

Parts of Speech

Knowing the parts of speech can help you use words correctly. **Verbs** tell what is or was happening. **Nouns** tell who or what a sentence is about.

Verbs:	grabbed	compete	struggled	defeated
Nouns:	weaknesses	control	goals	

Write four sentences. For each sentence, use one verb and one noun from the box. The first sentence has been done for you.

1. It is hard to compete without setting goals.

2. _____

3. _____

4. _____

Word Pyramid

struggled	compete	control	defeated

Write a sentence that connects a word from the box to the word *goal*.

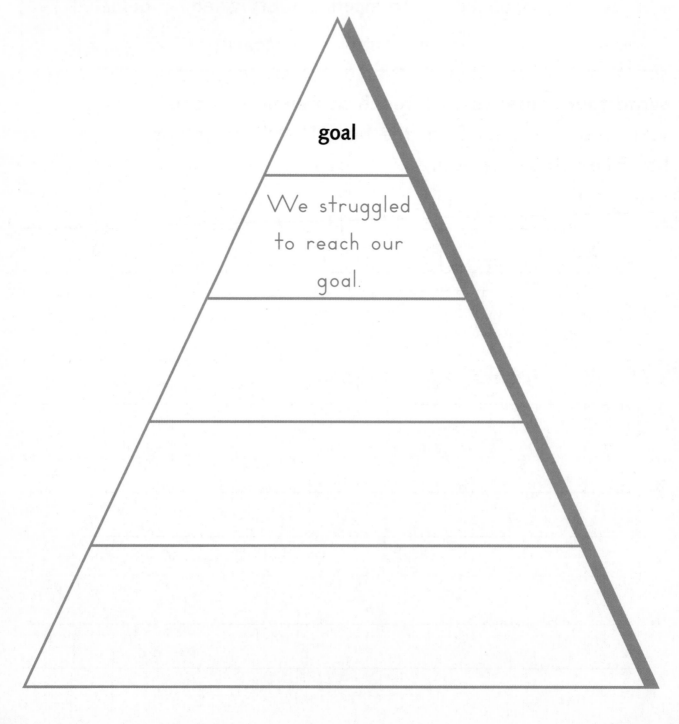

goal

We struggled to reach our goal.

Frequently Misspelled Words

Some words are misspelled because the letters in them sound like other letters.

been	going	head	work	coming
brother	said	very	really	sure

Fill in the consonants that are missing from these words. The first word has been done for you.

1. b r o t h e r

2. __ o __ i __ __

3. __ e __ __

4. __ o __ __

5. __ a i __

6. __ o i __ __

7. __ e e __

8. __ e a __ __ __

9. __ u __ e

10. __ e a __

Write five sentences, using a spelling word in each.

1. _____

2. _____

3. _____

4. _____

5. _____

Visualize

When you **visualize**, you make a picture in your mind. This helps you understand what you read.

To visualize:

* Use what you read

* Use what you know

Read the story. Make pictures in your mind.

Zeus was the Greek god of the sky. One day he looked down and saw something that made him very angry.

Zeus shook his fists and threw lightning bolts toward Earth. Then he roared and made the skies shake with thunder. Zeus became so angry that the clouds grew dark and heavy. Then the rain poured down. The people ran for their homes like frightened ants.

In the Text	Pictures in My Mind
Zeus looked down and saw something that made him angry.	a big, angry man standing in the clouds
The clouds grew dark and heavy, and the rain poured down.	huge, black clouds and pouring rain
People ran like frightened ants.	lots of people running

Read the story. Make pictures in your mind.

In Hawaii the goddess of fire is known as Pele. She has a bad temper and can make volcanoes erupt. Everyone tries not to make Pele angry.

One day a young boy stole one of Pele's favorite pieces of lava rock. Pele saw him carrying it across the volcano. Pele looked down into the mouth of the volcano. Inside the volcano the red liquid lava was boiling. It bubbled like a thick soup.

Pele let out a roar that shook the earth. The lava burst from the mouth of the volcano. It began to flow in fiery rivers down the side of the mountain. It raced over the cold, black lava. The boy turned around and saw that Pele was angry. He threw the piece of lava rock back. Then he ran as fast as he could!

In the Text	Pictures in My Mind

Use Multiple Strategies

Synonyms are words that have the same, or nearly the same, meaning.

middle	begin	present	lost	hurt

Rewrite each sentence. Replace the underlined word with a synonym from the box.

1. What time does the movie start?

_____

2. Put the flowers in the center of the table.

_____

3. I bought a gift for Mom's birthday.

_____

4. The boy's socks were missing.

_____

5. Littering will harm the environment.

_____

A **metaphor** compares two things that are not alike, such as *clouds* and *pillows*.

> The <u>clouds</u> in the blue sky are fluffy <u>pillows</u>.

Read the sentences. What two things are being compared? What does the sentence mean?

1. That child is a lamb. _____

_____

_____

2. Clair is a bear today. _____

_____

_____

3. Sam is a race horse. _____

_____

_____

4. Mary Lou is a ray of sunshine. _____

_____

_____

Before and After Reading

Read each statement. Write *T* if you think that the statement is *true* or *F* if you think it is *false*.

Before	**Anything Is Possible**	After
_____	**1.** The Paralympic Games are different from the Olympic Games.	_____
_____	**2.** Athletes use wheelchairs to race in the marathon.	_____
_____	**3.** Athletes who are blind do not compete in the games.	_____

Before	**To the Rescue!**	After
_____	**1.** Firefighters go to classes to learn more about firefighting.	_____
_____	**2.** Paramedics look for people who are lost.	_____
_____	**3.** Dogs help rescue teams find people.	_____

276

Before	Incredible Journeys	After
_____	**1.** A woman from England sailed around the world by herself.	_____
_____	**2.** You can get very sick climbing a high mountain.	_____
_____	**3.** It takes both physical and mental strength to survive challenges.	_____

Before	Breaking Through	After
_____	**1.** Hank Aaron was a great basketball player.	_____
_____	**2.** In the 1930s, African American players could not play baseball with white players.	_____
_____	**3.** Hank Aaron is famous because he hit so many home runs.	_____

Identify Cause and Effect

As you read, ask yourself why things happen.

- A **cause** explains why something happens.

- An **effect** is the result of what happens.

Read the story. Fill in the cause and the effect.

Tessie stared across the chessboard at Todd, her opponent. Todd was the best player in the chess club. Tessie tried to stay calm. She really wanted to win the match. She had practiced all her moves for weeks.

As the game went on, Todd took more and more of Tessie's pieces. Tessie began to worry that the match would be over soon. Todd wanted it to be over soon. He made a fast move without thinking. Tessie stared at the board in amazement. She reached out for her queen.

"Checkmate," she said with a smile on her face.

"Congratulations," Todd said. "You deserved to win."

Cause	Effect

Prepare to Present

Class Inquiry Question: _____

Circle one for each.

1. What does your research show?

2. How will you share your findings?

steps in a process

relationships

cause and effect

a story

how something works

Diagram
Book of Illustrations

Diagram   Skit
Puppet Show   Mural

Chart or Diagram
Skit
Puppet Show
Book of Illustrations

Picture Book
Skit
Puppet Show

Diagram
Mural
Picture Book

Think Back
Selection 4

Think about the people you read about. How did they use their strength and smarts to succeed?
Fill in the boxes.

Name of Person: _____

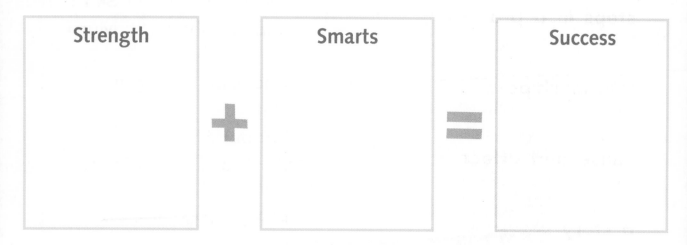

Strength		Smarts		Success
	+		**=**	

What does it take to overcome a challenge?
Write your answer.

_____

_____

_____

_____

Study the Model

Story

Read the Writing Model along with your teacher. Look for the beginning, middle, and end of the story.

Crossing the Creek
by Billy Katz

Ted and Leah stood by a gurgling creek, looking at a path on the other side. "What should we do?" asked Leah.

They had been hiking in the cool woods. Earlier that morning, they crossed the shallow creek on an old, squeaky bridge. But they must have missed it coming back. Now they were near the trailhead, but the water blocked their way.

Then Leah suggested that they jump over the creek. That sounded hard, so they practiced leaping over a huge log. There was no way they'd make it.

Suddenly, Leah's green eyes lit up. "Help me move this log!" she said. Ted and Leah pulled the rough, heavy log and pushed it into the water. Then they walked out on the log and jumped to the grassy bank. Ted and Leah made it home safe and dry.

Study the Model

Story

Read the Writing Model along with your teacher. Look for the beginning, middle, and end of the story.

Running the Bases
by Melanie Hatfield

Noah sat on the hard bench staring at the dusty baseball diamond. "I usually bat first. I get more hits. Why are you letting Rose bat first this game?" he asked the coach.

"Yes, you get more hits, but Rose is a smart batter. She gets walked more than you because she watches each pitch carefully. And she's fast. When she's on base, you can get a hit and bring her in to score," the coach explained.

Noah frowned and wondered how his coach's plan would work out, but he didn't wonder for long. In the very first inning, Rose got a walk and stole second base. Then Noah got a hit. He ran for first base like a lightning bolt and got there safely.

Noah heard cheers and turned to see the team giving Rose high fives. Wow, Rose scored, he thought. The coach was right!

Evaluation Rubric

Story

Writing Trait	Goals	Yes	Needs work!	Now it's OK.
Organization	My story has a beginning, middle, and end. I tell the events in the correct order.			
Ideas	My story has a problem that the characters solve.			
Voice	The voice is right for my audience.			
Word Choice	I use sensory details.			
Sentence Fluency	I combine sentences to make them less choppy.			
Conventions	All the words are spelled correctly. I use commas correctly.			

Peer Review

Story

Read your partner's paper. Then finish each sentence.

1. The problem in this story is

_____

_____

_____ .

2. The solution to the problem is

_____

_____

_____ .

3. A sensory detail in the story is

_____

_____

_____ .

Name of Reader _____

Commas

The chart shows where to use **commas**.

Commas	Example
between the day and the year	November 1, 2010
between the city and the state	Ann Arbor, Michigan
after the greeting and closing in a letter	Dear Mr. Rice, Sincerely,
between items in a series	I ate chicken, rice, and beans for dinner.

Add missing commas to the letter.

Dear Mr. Rosas,

I am writing to tell you that I won't be at the baseball game on April 23 2010. I am taking a trip to Houston Texas. I am going to see my aunt my uncle and my cousins.

I won't be able to pick up my new uniform. Could you please drop it off at my house?

Sincerely

Abby Bleeker

Often Confused Words

Some words sound the same but have different spellings and meanings.

two	I have **two** hands
too	I have a blue bike, **too**.
to	I rode my bike **to** the park.

there	Max and Louise are over **there**.
their	They are riding **their** bikes.
they're	**They're** riding fast.

Write the correct word in each sentence.
Use *two*, *too*, or *to*.

1. My family has ___two___ dogs.

2. I walk our dogs _____ the park.

3. My friend walks her dog, _____.

4. We are _____ girls with three dogs.

Write the correct word in each sentence.
Use *there*, *their*, or *they're*.

1. Other people walk _____ dogs in the park.

2. The dogs enjoy being _____.

3. _____ happy running and playing together.

4. If you have a dog, you should take it _____ too!

Taking Tests

Here is a question about *Turtle Races with Beaver.*

**Compare and contrast Turtle and Beaver.
Write about how they are alike and how they
are different.**

> How can you answer this question? First, look at the
> direction words.
>
> To **compare** means to think about how the characters
> are alike. To **contrast** means to think about how the
> characters are different.

**Make a list of the ways that Turtle and Beaver
are alike and different. The first connection has
been done for you.**

Alike	Different
Both live in a pond.	

Taking Tests

Here is a question about *My Lucky Day*.

Compare and contrast the fox and the piglet. Write about how they are alike and how they are different.

Alike	Different

Use your ideas from the chart to help you write your answer.

_____

_____

_____

_____

Inquiry Process

1. Generate Ideas and Questions

- Brainstorm Questions

- Decide on a Question

2. Make a Conjecture

3. Collect Information

- Share information

4. Confirm or Revise Your Conjecture

5. Share Findings

- Create Project

- Present Project

- Ask New Questions

Rules for Group Work

1. Be prepared to participate.

2. Listen quietly while other students are talking.

3. Cooperate with your group to finish each step.

4. Share materials and take turns.

5. Focus on your project.

6. Ask a partner questions when you do not understand.

Information Finder

How I Collect Information

Print
Books
Magazines
Picture Dictionaries
Encyclopedias
Atlases
Maps

Media
Television
Radio

Technology
Internet
LEAD21 eBooks

Interviews
Family
Teachers
Classmates

My Experiences
Watching and Listening
Remembering Things I've Done

Where I Collect Information

My Classroom
My School Library
My Public Library
At Home
My Community

Acknowledgments

Art Credits:

©The McGraw-Hill Companies, Inc., would like to thank the following illustrators for their contributions: Vera Tzepilova, Adele Jackson, Michael Bania, Thaw Naing, Stephanie Hans, Jago, Martin Jenkins, Jeffy James, Carol Swan, Elaine Nicholas, Deborah Borgo, Mike Laughead, Kat Chadwick, Peggy Rathmann, George Hamblin, Shane McGrath, Keiko Kasza, John Ardema, Spike Wademan, Linda Prater.

Photo Credits:

Cover (tl) ©Zschnepf/Shutterstock, (tr) ©Christian Musat/Shutterstock, (bl) Brand X Pictures/Jupiterimages, (br) Thomas Barwick/Getty Images; **2** ©Brand X Pictures; **6** ©DynamicGraphics/JupiterImages; **7** ©Library of Congress Prints & Photographs Division; **12** ©Susan LeVan/Getty Images; **14** (l) ©Marc Romanelli/Getty Images, (c) ©The McGraw-Hill Companies, (r) ©Thinkstock/Superstock, **16** ©Aurora Open/Peter Dennen/Getty Images; **20** ©Library of Congress; **21** (t) ©Lynn Betts, USDA National Conservation Service, (b) ©Jupiterimage/Brand X/Alamy; **22** (l) ©Library of Congress, (r) ©Pixland/PunchStock; **23** (l) ©Erica Simone Leeds, (r) ©GettyImages, **26** (l) ©Tony Anderson/GettyImages, (c) ©Creatas Images/Jupiterimages, (r) ©Hulton Archive/Getty Images; **38** ©Author's Image/PunchStock; **40** ©Vicky Kasala/Getty Images; **42** ©Royalty-Free/CORBIS; **43** ©Photo courtesy of USDA Natural Resources Conservation Service; **50** (l), (c) ©BrandXPictures/Jupiterimages, (r) ©The McGraw-Hill Companies; **53** ©Corbis/PunchStock; **54** ©Royalty-Free/CORBIS; **56** ©Photodisc/Getty Images; **57** ©Tony Anderson/Photodisc/Getty Images; **58** (tl) ©Comstock Images, (tr) ©BananaStock/Alamy, (br) ©Charles Smith/Corbis, (bl) ©Peter Adams/Getty Images; **60** (t) ©Bettmann/Corbis, (b) ©Charles Gullung/Cusp/Photolibrary; **61** (t) ©Andersen Ross/Getty Images, (b) ©Andersen Ross/Getty Images; **63** ©The McGraw-Hill Companies, Inc./Andrew Resek; **76** ©BananaStock/PunchStock; **78** ©Image Source/SuperStock; **79** ©Digital Vision; **84** ©McGraw-Hill Companies; **86** (t) ©Thinkstock Images Image/Jupiterimages, (c) ©Goodshoot Image/Jupiterimages, (b) ©Photos.com/Jupiterimages; **88** ©The McGraw-Hill Companies; **93** ©Image Source/PunchStock; **94** (tl) ©Royalty-Free/CORBIS, (tr) ©Royalty-Free/CORBIS, (br) ©Digital Vision/Getty Images, (bl) ©NPS Photo by Jim Peaco; **95** (tr) ©Getty Images/Photodisc, (tl) ©Medioimages/PunchStock, (cr) ©Design Pics Inc./Alamy Images, (cl) ©Digital Vision/Alamy, (br) ©Royalty-Free/CORBIS, (bl) ©image100/PunchStock; **98** (l) ©Photos.com/Jupiterimages, (c) ©KevinSchafer/Getty Images, (r) ©Adam Jones/Getty Images; **108** ©Robert Clay/Alamy; **113** ©Creatas/PunchStock; **114** (t) ©DLILLC/Corbis, (b) ©Veer; **115** (t) ©Jeremy Woodhouse/Getty Images, (c) ©PhotoLink/Getty Images, (b) ©Thinkstock/Getty Images; **122** (t) ©Comstock Images/Jupiterimage, (c) ©Photos.com/Jupiterimages; (b) ©liquidlibrary/Jupiterimages; **125** ©JupiterImages/Brand X/Alamy; **126** ©DigitalVision/Getty Images; **150** ©Royalty-Free/CORBIS; **152** (t) ©Mazer Creative Services, (b) ©Comstock Images/Jupiter Images/Alamy; **153** (t) ©Stockbyte/GettyImages, (c) ©BananaStock/Alamy, (b) ©Photodisc/PunchStock; **158** (t) ©Ken Chernus/GettyImages, (c) The McGraw-Hill Companies, (t) ©Photos.com/Jupiterimages; **160** ©Comstock Images/Jupiterimages; **165** ©David Buffington/Photodisc/GettyImages; **166** (l) ©Brand X Pictures, (r) ©Royalty Free/Corbis; **167** ©Royalty-Free/Corbis; **170** (t) ©Yellow Dog Productions Inc./GettyImages, (c) ©Amanda Hall/Getty Images, (b) ©ThinkstockImage/Jupiterimages; **184** ©Photodisc; **185** ©The McGraw-Hill Companies; **186** (t) ©Spike Mafford/Getty Images, (b) ©Royalty-Free/Corbis; **187** (t to b) ©The McGraw-Hill Companies, ©Brand X Pictures/Alamy, ©Image100/PunchStock, ©Royalty Free/Corbis; **194** (t) ©DigitalVision/Getty Images, (c) ©Thinkstock Image/Jupiterimages, (b) ©Comstock Images/Jupiterimages; **196** ©Getty Images/Photodisc; **201** ©1996 PhotoDisc Inc./Getty Images; **202** ©SW Productions/Brand X Pictures/Getty Images; **203** (t) ©SW Productions/Brand X Pictures/Getty Images, (b) ©Royalty-Free/Corbis; **204** (t) ©Mitch Epstein/Getty Images, (b) ©Stockxpert/Jupiterimages; **205** (t) ©Kevin Burke/Corbis, (b) ©Comstock Images/Jupiterimages; **206** ©Jack Star/PhotoLink/Getty Images; **218** ©Polka Dot Images/Jupiterimages; **222** © SuperStock Inc; **223** ©Ken Karp for MMH; **224** (t) ©Blend Images/GettyImages, (b) ©PhotoLink/GettyImages; **225** (t) ©John A. Rizzo/GettyImages, (c) ©RubberBall, (b) ©The McGraw-Hill Companies, Inc./Jill Braaten; **230** ©liquidlibrary Image/Jupiterimages; **232** ©GettyImages; **236** ©Photodisc/PunchStock; **237** ©Comstock/PunchStock; **240** ©Royalty-Free/Corbis; **242** ©The McGraw-Hill Companies; **252** ©Grant Faint/Getty Images; **257** ©2009 Jupiterimages Corporation; **258** ©Joseph Sohm/Visions of America/Corbis; **259** (t) ©mylife photos/Alamy, (c) ©Joshua Ets-Hokin/Getty Images, (b) ©Photodisc Collection/Getty Images; **266** (t) ©Getty Images, (c) ©ThomasBarwick/Getty Images, (b) ©Photodisc Inc/GettyImages; **276** (t) ©AFP/Getty Images, (b) ©Monkey Business Images; **277** (t) ©Ltd/Photolibrary, (b) ©Getty Images.